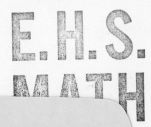

The Theory of Numbers

The Theory of Numbers

• BURTON W. JONES •

Professor of Mathematics, The University of Colorado

Rinehart & Company, Inc.

New York

Preface

Though mathematicians in their publications like to present their subject as if it were a deductive science, they will readily admit that back of their postulates and theorems are methods of discovery which are largely inductive. Postulates are not arbitrarily made but are constructed so that certain desirable consequences will follow. Proofs validate conjectures already made on the basis of experience and experiment. In fact, discovery of correct results often follows the sequence: A guess on the basis of experiment, an attempt at proof which fails but suggests a modified guess, which leads to another attempt at proof, and so on. One of the charms of mathematics is the pervading spirit of discovery. It was with these things in mind that this book was written.

Throughout, a definite effort is made to encourage and equip the student to make discoveries for himself. For the most part, reasons for postulates are developed before they are formulated. The statement and proof of some of the more important theorems are left to the student after preparation in similar situations. Problems are presented and a theory developed to answer the question raised, beginning especially in the second chapter.

First, this book makes no attempt to take the place of the teacher. It is, rather, his instrument. For instance, at the beginning, postulates and definitions are stated for the natural numbers. It is to be expected that the class will begin rather by formulating its own postulates and definitions and, on reference to the text, will find that its own are essentially equivalent to those printed. The limitations of a book for such a method are apparent. The text is not supposed to be "read like a novel." One recommended method is for the student to conceal the proof of a theorem and try to give one himself; failing that, he can reveal the first two lines and try to proceed from there. This is a slow, but excellent, way of laying a firm foundation. An attempt is made to give material in some detail at first but less so later on in the hope that by that time the student will have acquired greater facility.,

In any case, the pace should be very slow throughout the book. The author found, for instance, that the first chapter required about twenty class periods. Most of the book has been tried out in a classroom at one time or another.

In writing the first three chapters of the book the author partly had in mind those who are planning to teach in secondary and elementary schools. They need discussion of the number system which, after all, forms the basis for algebra as well as the manipulations of numbers themselves. Number theory contains countless interesting facts, which can be used to enliven and clarify elementary teaching of mathematics. For instance, repeating decimals can well be used when the elementary student first comes face to face with division by a decimal fraction. Equations with integer solutions arise from many puzzle problems as well as from the desire of a teacher to make her problems "come out right." In short, the first three chapters especially are rich in material useful for the secondary and elementary school teacher.

This book also gives an adequate introduction to the theory of numbers and its methods for those students majoring in mathematics or beginning graduate work. When used for such students much of the first chapter may be omitted. If taken slowly, it should be of assistance in bridging the gap between problem-solving mathematics and mathematics which develops a theory.

Careful reading of the manuscript by Dr. Carroll V. Newsom and Dr. Aubrey J. Kempner has resulted in many improvements which the author acknowledges with deep gratitude.

The theory of numbers seems to have a fascination for the layman and mathematician alike. It is hoped that this book may add to the multitude of its disciples.

BURTON W. JONES
The University of Colorado

January, 1955

Contents

•3• *Diophantine Equations*

•4• *Continued Fractions*

•5• *Nonlinear Congruences*

•6• *Quadratic Residues*

The Theory of Numbers

· 1 ·

The Development of the
Number System

1.1. Introduction

The theory of numbers concerns itself with the properties of integers or whole numbers; and, because it is concerned with integers, it has on the one hand the intrinsic interest that is associated with the solution of puzzles and on the other hand the inherent difficulty imposed by the restriction to integers. This explains the fact not only that amateurs play with the theory of numbers more than with any other branch of mathematics but also that most mathematicians have at various times worked in this field.

Some results in number theory are easy to state and easy to prove. For example, it is true that if any integer is subtracted from its cube, the result is divisible by 6; that is, $x^3 - x$ is divisible by 6 if x is an integer. This is true, since

$$x^3 - x = (x - 1)x(x + 1).$$

This equation shows that $x^3 - x$ is the product of three consecutive integers. At least one of these integers must be even and at least one divisible by 3, which shows that the product is divisible by 6.

Some results are easy to state but hard to prove. For example, recall that a **prime number** is an integer greater than 1 which is divisible only by itself and 1, the first ten prime numbers being

$$2, 3, 5, 7, 11, 13, 17, 19, 23, 29.$$

(An integer greater than 1 and not a prime is called **composite**.) Bertrand's postulate states that between any number greater than 1 and its double there is at least one prime number. For instance, between 3 and 6 is the prime 5, between $\sqrt{2}$ and $2\sqrt{2}$ is the prime 2. This general fact has been proved, but the proof is rather long and difficult.

Some rather apparent conjectures are easy to state but have not been proved; in fact, what amounts to the same thing to a mathematician, we do not know whether or not they are true. For instance, two primes are called **twin primes** if they differ by 2. Thus 3 and 5, 11 and 13, and 17 and 19 are twin primes. Is there a largest couple of twin primes? No one knows, though there is good evidence to support the belief that there is none.

Some propositions are hard to understand and hard to prove, such as the following: Two quadratic forms are congruent in the rational field if they are congruent in the field of reals and in all p-adic fields. There is no point in trying to explain this here.

Instead of presenting a theory to the student in this book, every effort is made to encourage him to approach the subject from certain leading problems in the hope that he can to a large extent under such guidance develop much of the theory himself. Though on many occasions the solutions to exercises in one section may be found in the next, it is to be hoped that the student will not attempt to read in advance but will try to solve the exercises, using only what has gone before. In that way he will not only make the subject more interesting because it is his own but will find his grounding more sure.

Moreover, the emphasis here is not on solving numerical exercises but in exploring the properties of numbers. These results can be stated most clearly in the form of theorems and corollaries. The function of the exercises is to illustrate the theory, to find new results, or to lead to conjectures on the basis of numerical evidence which may later be established by proof. The mathematician's exploration often takes the form of guessing results from one kind of evidence or another and then validating the guesses by proof. In this chapter we shall explore the fundamental properties of numbers beginning with the integers.

1.2. Fundamental properties of natural numbers

The **natural numbers** sometimes called **positive integers** are what we use to count with. For instance, the number which we call three is the most important thing common to three hats, three houses, and three lives. The system of natural numbers: 1,2,3,4,5,6, ⋯ is a universal tally device by which we can tell whether there are more things in one category than in another. It is an abstraction independent of the language we use to describe it. There is no great point in trying to define natural numbers beyond this; we may regard it as an undefined concept which we assume everyone understands.

Thus with each set of objects we can associate a natural number which describes **how many** objects are in the set. The natural numbers associated in this way with two sets A and B will be said to be the same if we can set up a **one-to-one correspondence** between the objects of A and those of B, that is, so that each object of A has one and only one "mate" in B and there are no "bachelors" nor "spinsters." For instance, a good way to discover if there are just as many boys as girls in a party is to form a procession with each boy taking a girl. If there are no boys or girls left without partners, we know that the number of boys is equal to the number of girls. Furthermore, no matter how partners were chosen, this result would be the same. In general, then, if such a correspondence can be established, the natural number associated with one set will be the same as (that is, equal to) that associated with the other.

Equality of natural numbers has four fundamental properties:

1. For any natural number a, it is true that $a = a$ (reflexive).
2. If $a = b$, then $b = a$ (symmetric).
3. If $a = b$ and $b = c$, then $a = c$ (transitive).
4. For any a and b, either $a = b$ or $a \neq b$ (determinative). In each case a,b,c are assumed to be natural numbers.

Addition of two numbers can be defined as follows: If the number of things in one set is c and in another set is d, then we call the number of things in both sets together the sum of c and d, and write it $c + d$. As a result of this definition and those above, addition has four properties:

1a. The sum of two natural numbers is a natural number (closure).
2a. If $a = b$, then $a + c = b + c$ (addition is well defined).
3a. $a + b = b + a$ (addition is commutative).
4a. $(a + b) + c = a + (b + c)$ (addition is associative).

The commutative property holds, since the order in which we count the two sets makes no difference in the sum, and the closure property 1a follows from our definition of natural number in terms of counting. For the associative property as shown above, if we denote by A,B,C, sets associated with the numbers a,b,c, respectively, we on the one hand combine C with the combination of A and B, while on the other hand we combine A with the combination of B and C. Again our definition shows that the results are the same.

Multiplication of two natural numbers can be defined as follows: If there are b sets of things with c things in each set, we define "b times c" or "the product of b and c" to be the total number of things in the b sets. The product of b and c is written $b \times c$, $b \cdot c$ or merely bc. Schematically, if we arrange the b sets in rows we have

c things

```
           .  .  .  .  .  .  .  .  .  .  .  .  .  .  .
           .  .  .  .  .  .  .  .  .  .  .  .  .  .  .
b sets     .  .  .  .  .  .  .  .  .  .  .  .  .  .  .
           .  .  .  .  .  .  .  .  .  .  .  .  .  .  .
```

Then "b times c" is understood to be that number obtained by counting by rows the total number of dots in the rectangular array. In the first place, the result must be a natural number (the closure property). Secondly, $a = b$ implies $ac = bc$, since then a rows of c dots will contain just as many dots as b rows of c dots. Thirdly, we could count the dots by columns which would be "c times b" which shows that the commutative property for multiplication holds.

In order to deal with the associative property of multiplication, consider a stack of trays of glasses in a cafeteria. Suppose there are r trays each having s rows of glasses with t glasses in each row. Then by our definition, the number of glasses on each tray would be st. Thus we have r trays of st glasses, that is, r sets with st in each set, and the total number of glasses would be $r(st)$. On the other hand, if we look at the stack from the front we will see r rows of glasses with s in each row, that is rs glasses; this will be repeated t times as we go back from the front. Thus we will have $(rs)t$ different glasses. Thus we have $r(st) = (rs)t$, the associative property for multiplication.

Finally, there is a property involving both processes, the distributive property: $a(b + c) = ab + ac$. We leave the proof of this in terms of counting as an exercise. Note that the commutative property of multiplication implies also that $ab + ac = (b + c)a = ba + ca$.

To summarize, we have given for natural numbers

Definitions: natural number, equality, addition, multiplication.

PROPERTIES	ADDITION	MULTIPLICATION
Well defined	$a = b$ implies $a + c = b + c$	$a = b$ implies $ac = bc$
Closure	sum of two natural numbers a natural number	product of two natural numbers a natural number
Commutative	$a + b = b + a$	$ab = ba$
Associative	$(a + b) + c = a + (b + c)$	$(ab)c = a(bc)$
Distributive		$ab + ac = a(b + c)$
		$ba + ca = (b + c)a$

Throughout the above table the letters stand for natural numbers. We shall find that the properties are shared by other kinds of numbers if equality, addition, and multiplication are properly defined. Notice that multiplication and addition are not interchangeable in the distributive property; that is, $a + (bc) \neq (a + b)(a + c)$.

Exercises 1.2

1. Which of the above properties are used in adding a column of figures? Explain.

2. Prove the distributive property from the definitions given.

3. What are some of the undefined terms in the section above?

4. Which of the above properties make the following expressions unambiguous:

$$a + b + c, \; abc?$$

5. Using only the above properties, show that $(a + b) + (c + d) = (a + [b + c]) + d$. Point out at each stage exactly what property is used. What expression does this make unambiguous?

6. What common axiom in plane geometry is expressed by the third property of equality listed above?

7. Which of the following have the four properties listed above for equality of natural numbers: (a) is the son of; (b) is the brother of; (c) is in the same family as; (d) is congruent to. Explain. For example, in case (a) the reflexive property would hold if "A is the son of B" implies "B is the son of A."

1.3. Inequalities

Suppose we have two sets of objects, namely, A, containing a objects, and B, containing b objects. We say that a is **greater than** b (written $a > b$) if we have to add some objects to the set B to have just as many things as there are in A. More precisely, we give the definition: $a > b$ means: $b + x = a$ is solvable for some natural number x. The symbol is read: a is greater than b.

Another way to express the relationship, a greater than b, is to say: b is less than a, that is, $b < a$. Both $>$ and $<$ are symbols of inequality and have the following properties expressed in terms of **greater than** for the natural numbers a, b, and c:

1. One of the following and only one must hold:
$$a > b, a = b, a < b.$$
2. If $a > b$ and $b > c$, then $a > c$ (the transitive property).
3. If $a > b$, then $a + c > b + c$ and $ac > bc$.

To prove the first property suppose, for instance, that both $a = b$ and $a > b$. Then, from the definition of inequality, there is a natural number c, such that $a = b + c$. But $a = b$, by hypothesis, and hence by the transitive property of equality, $b = b + c$. But we cannot set up a one-to-one correspondence between $b + c$ objects and b objects. Thus we cannot have both $a = b$ and $a > b$. The rest of the first property can similarly be established.

Before proceeding with the proof of the second property it may be well to consider the type of argument used in the previous paragraph — a form of argument which goes by the name **reduction to absurdity** or its Latin equivalent *reductio ad absurdum*. This has its basis in the axiom of logic that if P is true and P implies Q then Q must be true. It follows that if P implies something which is false then P must itself be false. There are many examples of such arguments outside of the field of mathematics. One example would be the following: "I know John has not left the house since the snowfall, since if he had there would have been tracks in the snow and there are none." In order to establish the desired result, it was supposed false and shown that such a supposition would have false consequences.

The second property may be proved as follows: $a > b$ and $b > c$ imply the existence of natural numbers x and y such that $a = b + x$ and $b = c + y$. Then, by use of the well-defined property of addition, we may replace b in the first equation by $c + y$ and have $a = (c + y) + x = c + (y + x)$ by the associative property. However, $y + x$ is a natural number by the closure property, and it may be designated by z. This shows that $a = c + z$ and hence $a > c$.

The third property we leave as an exercise.

We shall also use on occasion the symbols $a \geqq c$ or $a \geq c$ to mean "a is greater than or equal to c," that is, "a is not less than c." We also have the corresponding symbol with the inequality reversed.

1.4. Cancellation properties

The well-defined property of addition showed us that if $b = c$ then $a + b = a + c$. The converse of this statement is what we call the cancellation property; that is,

5a. If $a + b = a + c$, then $b = c$.

This may be proved as follows: If b is not equal to c, then, by the first property of inequalities, b must either be greater than c or less than c. We may without loss of generality assume that b is greater than c, that is, for some natural number d, $b = c + d$. Then $a + b = a + c$ becomes $a + c + d = a + c$, which, as we have seen, is impossible. This establishes the cancellation property of addition.

Similarly, for multiplication the cancellation property is

5m. If $ab = ac$, then $b = c$.

The proof is left as an exercise.

1.5. Critique

Some readers may be made uneasy by the above formulations, for there are many undefined terms and concealed assumptions (for instance, we considered glasses on trays). Though in the most rigorous treatment it is not possible to eliminate all such things, there is another way of defining the positive integers due to Peano, an Italian mathematician of the nineteenth century, which is much more precise in that the assumptions are reduced to a minimum. His axioms may be formulated as follows:

1. There is a natural number 1.
2. Every natural number b has a unique successor, which is also a natural number and which we call b^+; also b is called the predecessor of b^+.
3. The integer 1 has no predecessor.
4. If $a^+ = b^+$, then $a = b$.
5. Addition is defined by $a + 1 = a^+$ and $a + b^+ = (a + b)^+$.
6. Multiplication is defined by $a \cdot 1 = a$, $a \cdot b^+ = ab + a$.
7. (The induction postulate) A set of natural numbers A must include all the natural numbers if it has the following properties:
   a. A contains the number 1.
   b. The successor of any number of A is also in A.

From these assumptions all the above properties of natural numbers, and many others, may be proved. The uneasy reader might be interested to see to what extent he can do this.

The last axiom above deserves special attention, for it allows us to use the method of proof by induction. This can be seen by taking the set A to be the set of integers for which a certain theorem is true. Then, to show that the theorem is true for all integers, that is, that A contains all integers, we must show both of the following:

1. The theorem is true for the number 1.
2. If the theorem holds for any number of A, then it holds for the successor of that number.

For example, consider the following important

Theorem 1.5. If a is a natural number and b is another natural number not greater than a, then one of the following holds:

$$a = qb,$$
$$a = qb + r, \ r < b,$$

where q and r are natural numbers.

We prove this by induction on a. It is certainly true if $a = 1$, since the requirement that $b \le a$ implies $b = 1$ and $q = 1$.

Now, suppose the theorem is true for the predecessor of a, that is, $a - 1$. We shall prove it true for a. By our assumption, one of the following holds:

(1) $$a - 1 = qb,$$
(2) $$a - 1 = qb + r, \, r < b.$$

First, if (1) holds, then $a = ab + 1$. It follows that either $b = 1$ and $a = (q + 1)b$, which is the first case of the theorem, or $1 < b$, which is the second case.

Second, if (2) holds, we have

$$a = qb + r + 1.$$

Then, if $b = r + 1$, we have $a = (q + 1)b$, which is the first case of the theorem. If $b > r + 1$, the second case of the theorem holds. Thus our proof is complete.

Third, we assumed in the above cases that $b \le a - 1$. If this is not the case and $b \le a$, then $b = a$, and the theorem trivially holds.

An immediate consequence of the theorem is

Corollary 1.5. If b is a natural number less than a, then there is a unique natural number q such that

$$qb \le a \text{ and } (q + 1)b > a.$$

The number q of this corollary is called the **greatest integer in** a/b and is written $q = [a/b]$.

Exercises 1.5

1. Complete the proof of the first property of inequalities.

2. Prove the third property of inequalities.

3. Prove the cancellation property of multiplication.

4. Show how the corollary above follows from the theorem.

5. Show how the postulates of Peano may be used to prove the associative property of addition. HINT: For property 4a, use induction on c.

6. Show that if a and b are natural numbers, then $ab \geqq a$.

7. What properties do inequality and equality have in common?

8. Show by induction or otherwise that any set of natural numbers, finite in number, contains a greatest natural number.

9. Let $a_1, a_2, a_3, \cdots, a_k$ be a sequence of natural numbers such that each is less than the one which precedes it. Show that $k \leqq a_1$, in other words, that the number of numbers in the sequence cannot be greater than the first number.

1.6. Zero, subtraction

We have defined $a > b$ to imply the existence of a natural number c such that $a = b + c$. We then, by definition, say that c is a "minus" b; that is,

$$a = b + c \text{ means } a - b = c.$$

This is appropriate, since, by the cancellation property of addition, there is exactly one number c which, when added to b, gives a. ($a = b + c'$ would imply $b + c' = b + c$, and hence, by the cancellation property, $c' = c$.) Notice that $a - b$ is defined only if a is greater than b.

It is convenient to define a number, zero, by the equation

$$0 + a = a + 0 = a.$$

Then, if the definition of inequality is to be extended to include zero, we see that every natural number b is greater than zero because $0 + x = b$ has the solution $x = b$. Furthermore, as in Section 1.4, we can prove the cancellation property of addition for natural numbers and zero; that is, zero is the only number which, when added to a number, leaves it unaltered. Hence we may define $a - a$ to mean zero. If zero is to be included in the numbers which have the distributive property, we must define multiplication by zero in such a way that

$$ab = (a + 0)b = ab + 0 \cdot b.$$

Hence we must have $0 \cdot b = 0$. Thus we define

$$0 \cdot b = b \cdot 0 = 0.$$

We have discussed sets having n objects for any natural number n. It is convenient to define a null set as one similarly associated with the number zero. Thus the fact "No normal cat has two heads," could be stated as follows: The set of normal cats having two heads is a null set. Similarly, if there are no cows in pasture A, we could say that the cows in pasture A form a null set. It follows that if A contains a objects and B is a null set then the set obtained by combining A and B has $a + 0$ objects, that is, a objects. Also $b \cdot 0$ would be the number of objects in b null sets, which is zero. However, there seems to be no very satisfactory interpretation along the same lines of the product $0 \cdot b$. The most satisfactory way of thinking of zero is merely as a number having the properties

$$0 + a = a + 0 = a, \, 0 \cdot b = b \cdot 0 = 0.$$

Of course there is always the possibility that several requirements which we place on a new number may lead to a contradiction. However, we shall here assume that no such contradiction exists. It can be shown that the above definitions of addition of zero and multiplication imply all the properties listed for natural numbers in Section 1.2.

With the use of zero, Theorem 1.5 can be stated in a different way:

Theorem 1.6. For any "numbers" a and b, there are numbers q and r such that

$$a = qb + r, \, r < b.$$

Here the word "number" shall include all natural numbers and zero, except that we exclude $b = 0$.

1.7. Negative integers

If we confine ourselves to the natural numbers and zero, the expression $a - b$ has meaning only if b is equal to a or less than a. This is an unnatural restriction which it is convenient to eliminate. We do so by the introduction of negative integers, as follows: If b is a natural number or zero, we define a number ^-b by the equations

(1) $$b + {}^-b = {}^-b + b = 0,$$

and we shall say that $^-b = {}^-c$ if and only if $b = c$. Thus

(2) $$^-0 = 0, \text{ since } 0 + 0 = 0.$$

These new numbers exclusive of 0 we call negative integers.

First, it is necessary to define addition for these new numbers. If the associative and commutative properties of addition are to hold, addition of two negative numbers will require the following:

$$^-a + {}^-b + (a + b) = (a + {}^-a) + (b + {}^-b) = 0.$$

On the other hand,

$$^-(a + b) + (a + b) = 0.$$

Thus

$$^-a + {}^-b + (a + b) = {}^-(a + b) + (a + b).$$

and, if the cancellation property of addition is to hold, we must define

(3) $$^-a + {}^-b = {}^-(a + b).$$

To define the sum of a natural number and a negative integer we need to consider two cases. Suppose $a \geq b$, then, by the definition of $a - b$, we have $(a - b) + b = a$, and hence we must define $a + {}^-b$ so that

$$a + {}^-b = [(a - b) + b] + {}^-b = (a - b) + (b + {}^-b) = (a - b) + 0 = a - b.$$

Similarly, $^-b + a = a - b$. On the other hand, if $a < b$ we would need to define addition so that the following would be true:

$$a + {}^-b = a + (b - a) + {}^-(b - a) + {}^-b = {}^-(b - a) + b + {}^-b = {}^-(b - a).$$

Thus we define addition of a natural number and negative integer as follows:

(4)   If $a > b$, then $a + {}^-b = a - b = {}^-b + a$.
    If $a < b$, then $a + {}^-b = {}^-b + a = {}^-(b - a)$.

Thus we may replace $a + {}^-b$ by $a - b$ on the understanding that when b is greater than a, $a - b$ means the negative of $b - a$.

We wish the distributive law to hold for the new numbers, and hence

$$0 = (b + {}^-b)a = ba + ({}^-b)a = ba + {}^-(ba).$$

Thus we define multiplication as follows:

(5) $$({}^-b)a = a({}^-b) = {}^-(ab) = {}^-(ba),$$

where a and b are natural numbers or zero. It remains to define the product of two negative integers. We want to make this definition so that

$$0 = (b + {}^{-}b)({}^{-}a) = b({}^{-}a) + ({}^{-}b)({}^{-}a) = {}^{-}(ba) + ({}^{-}b)({}^{-}a) = {}^{-}(ba) + ba.$$

Hence we define

(6)
$$({}^{-}b)({}^{-}a) = ba = ({}^{-}a)({}^{-}b).$$

From these definitions (1) to (6) all the properties listed in Section 1.2 for the positive integers and zero follow for the negative integers.

We can now say for all integers that $a < b$ if there is a natural number c such that $a + c = b$. Thus, for instance, $-11 < -1$ since $-11 + 10 = -1$. If an integer is greater than zero, we call it **positive**.

The natural numbers, zero and the negative integers, together form what we call **the integers**. The set of positive integers coincides with the set of natural numbers.

Exercises 1.7

1. Show that Theorem 1.6 follows from Theorem 1.5.

2. Show that the definitions imposed on ${}^{-}b$ and the properties of positive integers imply for a, b, c.

   a. $a + {}^{-}b = c + {}^{-}b$ implies $a = c$.
   b. $({}^{-}a)b = ({}^{-}a)c$ implies $b = c$.

3. Justify ${}^{-}({}^{-}b) = b$. Is this a definition, or can it be proved?

4. Is subtraction of integers commutative? Is it associative? Is addition of integers commutative?

5. What properties of inequality listed in Section 1.3 hold for all integers including zero?

6. Do the cancellation properties of addition and multiplication hold for integers?

7. Does $a - b = a - c$ imply $b = c$ for integers a, b, c? Why or why not?

8. Simplify the following expression, pointing out at each step what properties of numbers you are using:

$$c(a + ba) - ac + a - abc.$$

Here a, b, c stand for integers.

9. Integers could be defined as pairs of natural numbers in the following way:

 a. $(a, b) = (c, d)$ means $a + d = c + b$.
 b. $(a, b) + (c, d)$ means $(a + c, b + d)$.
 c. $(a, b)(c, d)$ means $(ac + bd, ad + bc)$.

First, basing your proof upon accepted principles for natural numbers, show that addition and multiplication are associative and commutative. Second, show that

$$(x + a, a) + (b + b, b) = (x + y + a, a); \quad (a, a) + (b, c) = (b, c);$$
$$(1 + a, a)(b, c) = (b, c).$$

Third, show that

$$(x + a, a) + (a, x + a) = (a, a).$$

All the properties of negative integers may be derived from the three definitions. What number pairs correspond to zero? (Ref. 8, pp. 5 ff.) *

10. Prove that $a < b$ implies $a - c < b - c$.

1.8. Divisibility

If a and b are two integers, we say that a is divisible by b, or that a is a multiple of b, if there is an integer c such that $a = bc$. Note that we introduced negative integers so that the equation $a + x = b$ would always be solvable, but note that without introducing fractions we cannot say that $ax = b$ is solvable in all cases. When we deal solely with integers, the problem of divisibility is of fundamental importance. If we were talking about rational numbers (ratios of integers), there would be no problem of divisibility, since every number would be divisible by every other number provided the divisor were different from zero.

The notation often used for "b divides a" is $b|a$ and "b does not divide a" is written $b \nmid a$.

It is not hard to prove

Theorem 1.8a. If $a|b$ and $a|c$, then $a|b + c$ and $a|bc$.

Theorem 1.8b. If $a|b$ and $b|c$, then $a|c$.

---

* The reference numbers refer to the Bibliography in the back of the book.

Theorem 1.8c. If $a|b$ and $b|a$, where a and b are integers, then $a = b$ or $a = {}^-b$.

Every positive integer is divisible by itself and 1. Integers greater than 1 having no other divisors are called **prime numbers** or primes. Numbers greater than 1 which are not primes are called **composite.** Thus the natural numbers fall into three mutually exclusive categories:

1. The number 1,
2. The prime numbers,
3. The composite numbers.

Two numbers are called relatively prime (or one is prime to the other) if their only common divisors are 1 and −1. For instance, 6 and 35 are relatively prime, but 6 and 15 are not.

The prime numbers $2,3,5,7,11,13, \cdots$ are irregular in their distribution, and some of the deepest theorems in the theory of numbers, proved usually by delicate analysis, have to do with the prime numbers. For instance, it has been shown that

$$\lim_{x \to \infty} \pi(x)(\log_e x)/x = 1,$$

where $\pi(x)$ is the number of prime numbers less than x. That is, by taking x large enough, $\pi(x)(\log_e x)/x$ can be made as close as we please to 1. This is called the **prime number theorem.** Theorem 1.8g later in this section states that there is no last prime number. The proof is quite simple.

The greatest integer which divides two integers is called their **greatest common divisor,** often abbreviated g.c.d. For instance, the g.c.d. of 6 and −15 is 3. Using the notation (a,b) to denote the g.c.d. of a and b, we would have

$$(6, -15) = 3.$$

Though the above is perhaps the most natural way to define the g.c.d., there is another way which is sometimes more useful in proofs. Define g, the g.c.d. of two integers a and b, to be that positive integer which has the following two properties:

1. g divides both a and b.
2. Any number dividing both a and b also divides g.

That these two definitions yield the same number may be seen as follows: Let g_1 be the g.c.d. according to the first definition and g_2 according to the second. The first definition would then imply $g_2 \leq g_1$ and the second that g_1 would divide g_2. Hence $g_1 \leq g_2$, and it must follow that $g_1 = g_2$.

Both definitions can immediately be extended to any number of integers. For instance, we can write

$$(6, 21, 35) = 1.$$

That any pair of integers has a greatest common divisor can be shown from the first definition, for any divisor of a positive integer must be either the number itself or less than it; hence a positive number cannot have more than a finite number of divisors. Then, to find the greatest common divisor of two numbers, we need merely list their divisors and pick out the greatest one common to both. However, this means of finding the g.c.d. is laborious. There is a somewhat shorter method which depends on Theorem 1.6 above and the second definition of g.c.d., which is as follows:

Theorem 1.8d.   If a and b are two positive integers, then the process of Theorem 1.6 is repeated as follows:

$$a = qb + r_1, 0 \leq r_1 < b,$$
$$b = q_1 r_1 + r_2, 0 \leq r_2 < r_1,$$
$$r_1 = q_2 r_2 + r_3, 0 \leq r_3 < r_2,$$
$$\cdot \quad \cdot \quad \cdot \quad \cdot \quad \cdot \quad \cdot$$
$$r_{k-3} = q_{k-2} r_{k-2} + r_{k-1}, 0 \leq r_{k-1} < r_{k-2},$$
$$r_{k-2} = q_{k-1} r_{k-1} + r_k, 0 \leq r_k < r_{k-1}.$$

Eventually one of the r's will be zero, call it r_k, and suppose $r_{k-1} \neq 0$. Then r_{k-1} will be the g.c.d. of a and b. The process is called the **Euclid Algorithm.** (An "algorithm" is a term applied to a repetitive process like the above, used to achieve a desired result.)

First, let us see how this process works in a numerical case. Let $a = 228$ and $b = 177$. Then we have

$$228 = 1 \cdot 177 + 51,$$
$$177 = 3 \cdot 51 + 24,$$
$$51 = 2 \cdot 24 + 3,$$
$$24 = 8 \cdot 3 + 0.$$

The theorem states, thus, that 3 is the g.c.d. of 228 and 177.

To prove this, notice first that one of the r's must finally be zero, since, until we reach the point where one is zero, they form a decreasing sequence of positive integers. (See Exercise 9 of Section 1.5.) Thus the last equality will be

$$r_{k-2} = q_{k-1}r_{k-1} + 0,$$

and r_{k-1} divides r_{k-2}. Then Theorem 1.8a and

$$r_{k-3} = q_{k-2}r_{k-2} + r_{k-1}$$

imply that r_{k-1} divides r_{k-3}. We can continue to follow this back until in the first equation r_{k-1} divides r_1 and b and hence a. Therefore we have demonstrated that r_{k-1} divides a and b, the first requirement of g.c.d.

Since the first equation may be written $a - qb = r_1$, then any common divisor, d, of a and b divides r_1. Since d divides b and r_1 it must, from the second equation, divide r_2, and, continuing, we see that d divides r_{k-1}. Hence the second requirement of the definition is fulfilled, and we have proved Theorem 1.8d. We have climbed up the ladder and climbed down again.

There is still a third definition of g.c.d. which we include in the following:

Theorem 1.8e. Given two nonzero integers a and b, let r be the least positive integer expressible in the form

$$ax + by = r,$$

with x and y integers. Then r is the g.c.d. of a and b.

Again, using the second definition of g.c.d., we see that the second condition is satisfied, for Theorem 1.8a shows that any common divisor of a and b divides r. To show that r divides a and b, suppose that r does not divide a. Then

$$a = qr + s, \quad 0 < s < r.$$

Furthermore, there are integers x_0, y_0 such that $ax_0 + by_0 = r$, and $qr = qax_0 + qby_0$. However, $a = qr + s$ implies $qr = a - s = qax_0 + qby_0$. Hence $s = a(1 - qx_0) - bqy_0$. Thus s is a positive integer less than r, representable in the form $ax + by$, with $x = 1 - qx_0$ and $y = -qy_0$. This result contradicts our assumption that r is the least integer so expressible and completes the proof.

We have the following important

Corollary 1.8e. If m divides ab and $(m,a) = 1$, then m divides b; for by the above theorem we know there are integers x and y such that $mx + ay = 1$, whence $m(bx) + y(ab) = b$. However, m divides $m(bx)$ and ab, which by Theorem 1.8a shows that m divides b.

Corollary 1.8e'. If m is prime to a and to b, then it is prime to ab; for, if m had a factor in common with ab, it would have a prime factor in common. Call this common prime factor p. By the first corollary, p would divide b, which would imply that m and b have a common factor in contradiction to the hypothesis.

These then yield the Fundamental Theorem of the theory of numbers:

Theorem 1.8f (The Fundamental Theorem). If a positive integer is factored into prime factors in two ways, as follows:

$$p_1 p_2 \cdots p_r = q_1 q_2 \cdots q_s,$$

where two or more p_i or two or more q_i may be equal, then $r = s$ and the factors p_i are equal to the factors q_i in some order. Briefly, we then say that decomposition into prime factors is unique except for order of the prime factors.

To prove this, notice that a prime either divides a number or is prime to it. Suppose p_1 is not equal to any of the q_i's. If this is true then it must be prime to each one and hence by Corollary 1.8e', to their product. This is not possible, since p_1 divides their product. Hence we may renumber the q_i if necessary and take $p_1 = q_1$. Then the cancellation theorem for multiplication shows that

$$p_2 p_3 \cdots p_r = q_2 q_3 \cdots q_s,$$

and we may deal with p_2 as we did with p_1. Continuing in this way we see that the theorem is true.

This theorem also shows that we can express any integer in the form

$$a = p_1^{a_1} p_2^{a_2} \cdots p_n^{a_n},$$

where now no two p_i are equal. This decomposition again is unique except for the order in which the prime factors are written. Suppose the only prime numbers dividing both a and b are

$$p_1, p_2, \cdots, p_n.$$

Then we can express a and b in the following forms:

$$a = p_1^{a_1} p_2^{a_2} \cdots p_n^{a_n} r_1^{v_1} r_2^{v_2} \cdots r_m^{v_m} \; ; b = p_1^{b_1} p_2^{b_2} \cdots p_n^{b_n} s_1^{w_1} s_2^{w_2} \cdots s_u^{w_u},$$

where no two of p_i, r_j, s_k are equal. The g.c.d. of a and b is equal to

$$p_1^{c_1} p_2^{c_2} \cdots p_n^{c_n},$$

where, for each i, c_i is the smaller of a_i and b_i. How would one express the **least common multiple** (l.c.m.) of a and b?

Any number which is divisible by 2 is called an even number, and all others are odd. If two numbers are both even or both odd, they are said to be of the same **parity**; if one is even and the other odd, they are said to be of opposite parity. Since every even number is of the form $2k$ for an integer k, and every odd number of the form $2k + 1$, it is not hard to see that the sum of two numbers of the same parity is even and that the sum of two numbers of opposite parity is odd.

Euclid proved that there is no greatest prime number, that is, there is an infinity of prime numbers. We may state it in the following way, and we shall give Euclid's proof.

Theorem 1.8g. For any positive integer n there are more than n primes.

To prove this, suppose that there are only n primes and list them as follows:

$$p_1, p_2, \cdots, p_n.$$

Then form the number

$$N = p_1 p_2 \cdots p_n + 1.$$

If one of the n primes divided N, it would, by Theorem 8.1a, have to divide 1, which is impossible. Then either N is itself a prime, or it is divisible by a prime different from those listed. In either case there must be more than n primes.

The **least common multiple** of two integers a and b is defined to be the smallest positive integer which is divisible by both a and b. This statement is equivalent to the following: m is the least common multiple of a and b if it has two properties:

1. m is a multiple of a and b.
2. m divides every common multiple of a and b.

This bears some similarity to our second definition of g.c.d.

Exercises 1.8

1. Show that Theorem 1.8d implies the following: If the multiples of a are plotted in red on a line and the multiples of b in green, where a and b are positive integers with greatest common divisor g, then g will be the shortest distance from any green to any red point.

2. By the process of Theorem 1.8c find the g.c.d. of 576 and 73. Use this same process to find integers x and y so that $576x + 73y = (576, 73)$.

3. Prove Theorems 1.8a, 1.8b, and 1.8c.

4. If $(ab, p) = 1$, show that $p^{k+1}|ap^k + bp^s$ only when $k = s$ and $p|a + b$.

5. Show that $(a,b) = d$ implies $(a/d, b/d) = 1$.   Show that $a(b,c) = (ab, ac)$.

6. Prove that if $(a,b) = 1$ and r divides ab then $r = st$ where $s|a$ and $t|b$ and s and t are uniquely determined except for sign; s or t or both may be 1.

7. Prove that if ab/d is a multiple of a and b then d divides both a and b. Hence show that ab/d is the least common multiple of a and b if and only if $d = (a,b)$.

8. Prove that if a/b and c/d are two fractions in lowest terms, and if

$$\frac{a}{b} + \frac{c}{d} = \frac{ad + bc}{bd}$$

is an integer, then $b|d$ and $d|b$; that is, $b = \pm d$.

9. Prove that the sum of an even number of odd integers is even and the product of a set of integers is even unless they are all odd.

10. Prove that the product of an odd number of integers of the form $4n - 1$ is of the same form.

11. Using Theorem 1.6 with $b = 4$ show that every odd integer is of one of the forms $4n - 1$, $4n + 1$, and hence that if the product of an odd number of odd integers is of the form $4n + 1$ at least one is of the form $4n + 1$.

12. Extend the definition of least common multiple to more than two integers.

13. Show that every integer not divisible by 3 is of one of the forms

$3n + 1$ or $3n + 2$, and if an integer has the form $3n + 2$ at least one of its prime factors is of the form $3n + 2$.

14. Prove that N in Theorem 1.8g has at least one prime factor of the form $4n - 1$ and hence there is no greatest prime of the form $4n - 1$.

15. Theorem 1.6 shows that every integer s can be expressed in the form $ka + r$, for a given integer a, where $0 \leq r < a$. Which one of the following set of integers is divisible by a:

$$s, s + 1, s + 2, \cdots, s + a - 1?$$

Show that there is only one of the set divisible by a. In other words, any set of a consecutive integers contains exactly one multiple of a.

16. Use the result of the previous exercise to show that $x^5 - 5x^3 + 4x$ is divisible by 60 for every integer x.

17. For a given number of steps, k, in the Euclid Algorithm show that a and b will be the least if

$$r_k = 0, r_{k-1} = 1, r_{k-2} = 1, r_{k-3} = 2, r_{k-4} = 3, r_{k-5} = 5, \cdots,$$

where for each subscript i, $r_i = r_{i+1} + r_{i+2}$ and $q_i = 1$. Thus a and b would have to be two successive numbers in the sequence, the first ten terms of which are

$$0, 1, 1, 2, 3, 5, 8, 13, 21, 34.$$

That is, if the Euclid Algorithm process has five steps, the least pair of values of a and b is 8 and 13. Why does this imply that the Euclid Algorithm for (a,b) with $b < 34$ must contain less than 8 steps?

18. If $a = bq + r$ and $c = bt + s$, show that $a - c$ and $r - s$ are either both divisible by b or both not divisible and hence that the difference of two numbers is divisible by b if and only if their remainders when divided by b are equal.

19. Prove that if $f(x)$ is a polynomial with integer coefficients and if a is an integer not zero such that $f(a) = 0$ then a divides the constant term.

20. Prove that if p and q are integers and $p^2 = 2q^2$ then p and q are both even.

21. Prove that if $x^2 = ab$ where x,a,b are positive integers and $(a,b) = 1$ then there are integers y and z such that

$$yz = x, a = y^2 \text{ and } b = z^2.$$

22. Prove that if a and b have a common prime factor and $a^2 + b^2 = c^2$ then that common prime factor divides c. Would the same result necessarily hold if the word "prime" were omitted?

23. Prove that if $(b,c) = 1$ then $(b - c, b + c) = 1$ or 2. Under what conditions will the latter g.c.d. be 1? Answer the similar questions for $(b + 2c, 2b + c)$.

24. Show that the pair of equations, $ax + by = r$, $a'x + b'y = r'$, where all the letters stand for integers and $ab' - a'b = d \neq 0$, have integer solutions if and only if $rb' - r'b$ and $r'a - ra'$ are divisible by d.

25. If $a^2 = c^2 - b^2$, $(c,b) = 1$, and just one of c,b is even, use Exercise 21 to show that there are integers m and n such that $mn = a$, $c - b = m^2$, $c + b = n^2$.

26. If $(c, b) = 1$ and both c and b are odd, show that

$$a^2 = c^2 - b^2$$

implies that a is even. Show that $(c - b)/2$ and $(c + b)/2$ are relatively prime integers and equal respectively to m^2 and n^2, where m and n are integers whose product is $a^2/4$. Show how this may be used to give all solutions of

$$a^2 + b^2 = c^2,$$

where a is even, b is odd, and no two of a, b, c, have a common factor greater than 1.

27. The following illustrates for the numbers 35,15,12,6 a device for finding the l.c.m. of a set of numbers. Why does it work?

	35	15	12	6
3	35	5	4	2
5	7	1	4	2
2	7	1	2	1
7	1	1	2	1
2	1	1	1	1

Explanation: Since 3 divides three of the numbers, we use it for the first row. Where it is a divisor of the number in the line above, we place the quotient in the row; when it is not a divisor, we repeat the number above. Since 5 is a divisor of two numbers of the first row below the horizontal line, we use it next to obtain the second row. So we continue until a row consists entirely of ones. The l.c.m. is the product of the numbers in the left column, here 3,5,2,7,2. The order in which we divide by these numbers makes no difference to the result. However, at each step it is important to begin a row only with a prime divisor.

28. Prove that for any two integers a and b there are integers q and r such that

$$a = bq + r, \quad -b < 2r \leq b.$$

This forms the basis for the so-called **least remainder algorithm.** Carry this through for 576 and 73. Show that this process always yields the g.c.d.

29. Establish results similar to those of Exercise 17, but use the least remainder algorithm.

30. Show that "equivalence" in the following sense has the four properties of equality listed in Section 1.2: Given a fixed integer m, call "a equivalent to b" if $a - b$ is divisible by m, for integers a and b.

31. If $(a,m) = 1$, for what integers x will ax be "equivalent to" ab in the sense of the previous exercise, where b is also an integer?

1.9. The decimal notation

The properties of integers in the preceding sections are independent of what we call them. We say, "three divides six." If the Martians designated three objects by the word "glob" and six objects by the word "tocs" while our "divides" is pronounced by them "sots" then it would be equally true that "glob sots tocs." The corresponding result would hold, whatever the words or notation. However, some notation is necessary, and we are accustomed to the "decimal notation," associated with the number ten, since we have ten fingers, and say our number system "has the base ten."

If we had twelve fingers, we would undoubtedly employ the "duodecimal system," where the base would be twelve. If we had just eight fingers, it would be the "octic system," of base eight.

We have, in fact, just ten different symbols: $0,1, \cdots ,9$, and make the place where they occur important. For instance: 23 is understood to be 3 plus two tens and 576 is six, plus seven tens, plus five hundreds. Also

$$769301 = 1 + 0 \cdot 10 + 3 \cdot 10^2 + 9 \cdot 10^3 + 6 \cdot 10^4 + 7 \cdot 10^5.$$

The zero can be considered to indicate absence of the corresponding power of ten. Using letters, we could write

$$abcde = e + 10d + 10^2 c + 10^3 b + 10^4 a,$$

where a,b,c,d,e are the digits of the number. (We call the symbols, $0,1,2, \cdots, 9$ digits, since each can be associated with a finger of the hand, zero being a little finger.)

From this it follows that if the last digit of a number is divisible by 5, the number is also. Why? If the last digit is even, the whole number is divisible by 2, therefore, even. Why? If the last two digits form a number divisible by 4, why is the number divisible by 4? Why cannot one tell from the last digit whether or not a number written in the decimal system is divisible by 3?

If our number system had the base three we would need only the symbols $0,1,2$. Then $abcde$ would mean

$$e + 3d + 3^2 c + 3^3 b + 3^4 a,$$

and the number would be divisible by 3 if e were zero, but we could not tell from the last digit whether or not it would be divisible by 2.

In any system of notation the number for three would divide the number for six, but telling by inspection whether or not it is divisible would be easier in one notation than in another.

In some respects the number system to the base two, the so-called **binary system,** is the simplest. It has only two symbols: 0 and 1. It is especially adapted to machine calculation, since 0 can correspond to the lack of a certain electric connection and 1 can correspond to its existence. The addition table is merely

$$0 + 0 = 0, \, 0 + 1 = 1, \, 1 + 1 = 10,$$

and the multiplication table would be the joy of every schoolboy:

$$0 \cdot 0 = 0, \, 0 \cdot 1 = 0, \, 1 \cdot 1 = 1.$$

An example of multiplication would then be

$$
\begin{array}{r}
1011010 \\
101 \\
\hline
1011010 \\
0000000 \\
1011010 \\
\hline
111000010.
\end{array}
$$

The chief disadvantage of this notation is that it requires much writing for relatively small numbers. In the decimal notation the two numbers above would be 90 and 5, and the result, 450. To see this, notice that the digits in the binary form counting from the right indicate the presence (when 1 occurs) or absence (when 0 occurs) of the corresponding power of 2. Thus we can make a table for the numbers as follows:

Number to the base two	2^{11}	2^{10}	2^9	2^8	2^7	2^6	2^5	2^4	2^3	2^2	2^1	2^0
1011010						1	0	1	1	0	1	0
101										1	0	1
111000010		1	1	1	0	0	0	0	1	0

To find the decimal value of the first number we add the powers of 2 under which 1's occur: $2 + 8 + 16 + 64 = 90$. The decimal values of the other numbers may be found similarly.

One may convert from the decimal system to the binary system in a like manner. Suppose we wish to write 49 in the binary system. The highest power of 2 less than 49 is 2^5; hence $49 = 2^5 + 17$. Then $17 = 2^4 + 1$. Continuing in this fashion, we have $49 = 2^5 + 2^4 + 0 \cdot 2^3 + 0 \cdot 2^2 + 0 \cdot 2 + 1$, which, in the binary system, becomes 110001.

A convenient method of converting from the decimal system to the binary is indicated by the following process:

$$
\begin{array}{ccccccc}
0 & 1 & 3 & 6 & 12 & 24 & 49 \\
1 & 1 & 0 & 0 & 0 & 1 & .
\end{array}
$$

We write 49, the number to be converted, at the right and divide by 2, writing the quotient, 24, to the left of 49, and the remainder below it. Then we divide 24 by 2, writing the quotient, 12, to its left and the remainder, 0, below it. We continue in this way and see that 49 is 110001 in the binary system.

One application of the binary notation is in the so-called Russian Peasant method of multiplication. This is a method by which the product of any pair of integers may be found by a succession of divisions and multiplications by two and one addition.

The process for 375 and 39 is as follows:

39	375
19	750
9	1500
4*	3000
2*	6000
1	12000
	14625

In the left column we divided by 2, disregarding remainders, and in the right column multiplied by 2. In the left column we placed asterisks after the even numbers and, in the addition, omitted the numbers to the right of the stars. The reason for this process may be seen by writing 39 in the binary system, namely, 100111. Writing these in a column with the first digit at the bottom, it is seen that the asterisks correspond to the two zeros. Thus, to multiply 375 by 100111 in the binary system, we multiply 375 by 1, since the last digit for 39 is 1; multiply it by 2, since the next to the last digit for 39 is 1; multiply it by 4, since the third from the right digit of 39 is 1; we do not multiply it by 8 or 16, since those digits are zero, but we multiply it by 32. This is accomplished by the addition process above.

Exercises 1.9

1. Multiply 75 by 423 by the Russian Peasant method. Convert these numbers to the binary system, multiply and check by converting back to the decimal system.

2. Four cards are constructed. The first, headed 1, has all the odd numbers between 1 and 16; the second, headed 2, has the numbers: 2,3,6,7,10, 11,14,15; the third, headed 4, has the numbers: 4,5,6,7,12,13,14,15; the fourth, headed 8, has all the numbers from 8 to 15 inclusive. You ask someone to choose a number between 1 and 15 and to hand you the cards on which this number occurs. You then add the numbers at the tops of

those cards and tell him the number he chose. How would you number five cards to pick a number from 1 to 31? Why does it work?

3. Suppose, instead of wanting to answer "yes" or "no," it were to be one of "yes," "no," or "maybe." What number system would you use instead of the binary system? What assumptions about "yes," "no," and "maybe" would have to be made?

4. Translate 57 and 93 into the binary system, multiply them in that system, and check your result by converting into the decimal system.

5. Four weights are to be chosen so that any object from 1 to 15 pounds (weighing a whole number of pounds) could be weighed by putting the object in one pan of a balance scale and balancing it with a proper assortment of the four weights in the other pan. What would they be?

6. Show that if the weights above could be put in either pan, three weights would suffice for objects weighing less than 15 pounds. What would their weights be and how would the proper assortment be found for any object?

7. Exercise 2 is connected with the base two. Could similar cards be constructed for a trick using the base three?

8. Show that if the quotient when one divides a number by 2^3, disregarding the remainder, is odd then 1 is the fourth digit from the right in the binary representation of the number, while if the quotient is even, the fourth digit will be 0. Generalize this for any power of 2.

1.10. Rational numbers

Though the theory of numbers is primarily concerned with integers, there are a number of situations in which rational numbers are involved. Furthermore, the place of the integers in the number system can better be appreciated if we see how rational numbers occur.

Just as we introduced negative integers so that we could solve the equation $b + x = a$, when a is greater than b, so we determine a new kind of number, called a **rational number,** so that $bx = a$ will be solvable (when a and b are integers with $b \neq 0$), having the property that

(1)
$$(a/b)b = b(a/b) = a.$$

This we call a "rational number," since it is written as a "ratio." When $b = 0$ we cannot consistently define this symbol, as we shall see later. Whenever we write the symbol (a/b), we assume $b \neq 0$.

First, to define equality, consider the two rational numbers (a/b) and (c/d), where $bd \neq 0$. From the definition,

$$(a/b)b = a, \ (c/d)d = c.$$

Then, if multiplication is to be well defined, we have

$$(a/b)bd = ad, \ (c/d)db = cb;$$

and, if $(a/b) = (c/d)$, we must have $ad = cb$. On the other hand, if the cancellation property of multiplication is to hold, $ad = cb$ must imply $(a/b) = (c/d)$. We therefore make the following

Definition of equality: The rational numbers (a/b) and (c/d) are said to be equal whenever

$$(2) \qquad\qquad ad = bc, \ bd \neq 0.$$

An immediate consequence is the following

Cancellation property of fractions: $(a/b) = (ak/bk)$, $k \neq 0$, since $abk = bak$.

Since $(a/1)1 = a = a \cdot 1$, we would define

$$(3) \qquad\qquad (a/1) = a.$$

Hence all the integers are rational numbers. This includes $a = 0$.

Since we want the distributive and associative properties for multiplication to hold for rational numbers we need to have the following:

$$\begin{aligned}
\{(a/b) + (c/d)\} \cdot bd &= (a/b) \cdot bd + (c/d) \cdot bd \\
&= (a/b)b \cdot d + (c/d)d \cdot b \\
&= ad + cb,
\end{aligned}$$

where the first equality assumes the distributive property for rational numbers, the second the associative property for rational numbers and the commutative property for integers, and the last equality results from the definition of a rational number. However,

$$\{(a/b) + (c/d)\} \cdot bd = ad + cb,$$

which means that to be consistent we must define addition of rational numbers by

(4) $$(a/b) + (c/d) = (ad + cb)/bd.$$

Furthermore, we wish multiplication of rational numbers to be commutative and associative.

Hence

$(a/b) \cdot b = a$ and $(c/d)d = c$ should imply
$(a/b)b(c/d)d = (a/b) \cdot (c/d)bd = ac.$

However, by our definition of rational numbers, $(ac/bd)bd = ac$. Hence we define multiplication so that

(5) $$(a/b)(c/d) = (ac/bd).$$

These five definitions suffice to prove that rational numbers satisfy all the properties of integers listed in Section 1.2. Also

$$0 \cdot (a/b) = (0/1)(a/b) = (0/b) = 0 = (a/b) \cdot 0.$$

Thus zero multiplied by any fraction gives zero, by definition.

Now we can see why the exclusion of $b = 0$ in (a/b) is necessary if our rational numbers are to have the desired properties. Suppose we were to define $(1/0)$ to be a number called "infinity," and wrote

$$(1/0) = \infty, \text{ that is, } 1 = 0 \cdot \infty.$$

Then, by the cancellation property of fractions, $(2/0) = \infty$; that is, $2 = 0 \cdot \infty$. However,

$$2(0 \cdot \infty) = 2 \cdot 2 = 4 \text{ and } (2 \cdot 0) \infty = 0 \cdot \infty = 2.$$

Thus $4 \neq 2$ shows that $2(0 \cdot \infty) \neq (2 \cdot 0) \infty$, and hence the associative property would not hold. This shows that if we were to call $(1/0)$ a number it would be necessary to specify that it did not behave like the other numbers. It is much easier to exclude it from the family of numbers. We therefore say that $(1/0)$ is not a number. In fact $(a/0)$ is not a number. We do not even call it infinity, since that might be misleading.

We call a rational number positive if it is equal to a/b, where a and b are positive integers. It is called negative if a and b are integers of opposite sign (that is, one positive and one negative). Furthermore, if r and s are two rational numbers, we say that $r < s$ if there is a positive rational number u such that $r + u = s$. Subtraction of rational numbers is defined in the same manner as subtraction for integers.

Exercises 1.10

1. Show that the above definitions and the properties of integers imply that addition and multiplication of rational numbers are commutative and associative.

2. Show that equality of fractions has the properties of equality listed in Section 1.2.

3. Suppose we define $(a/b) = (c/d)$ whenever $c = ka$, $d = kb$ for k, a non-zero integer. Would the properties of equality then hold? If not, what would your answer be for k, a rational number?

4. Using only the properties and definitions of the last section, show that $a(1/b) = a/b$. Point out what properties are used.

5. If $r = (a/b)$, $s = (c/d)$, and s is not zero, define the symbol (r/s) to have the property that

$$(r/s)s = r.$$

What must r/s be in terms of a,b,c,d?

6. Show one property which would fail if we defined

$$(a/b) + (c/d) = (a + c)/(b + d).$$

7. Use Exercise 20 of Section 1.8 to show that there is no rational number whose square is 2.

8. What properties of integers listed in Sections 1.2 and 1.4 also hold for rational numbers?

9. Why does $(0/b) = 0$ follow from the properties listed for rational numbers?

10. Show that if a/b and c/d are two rational numbers where a,b,c,d are integers and b and d are positive then

$$a/b > c/d \text{ if and only if } ad > bc.$$

11. Show that if a/b and c/d are two rational numbers with b and d positive and $0 < a/b < c/d$ then $a/b < (a + c)/(b + d) < c/d$. Why does

this show that between any two distinct rational numbers there is always a third? Is this a property of integers?

12. Let $f(x)$ be a polynomial $a_nx^n + a_{n-1}x^{n-1} + \cdots + a_1x + a_0$ whose coefficients are integers. Let r and s be two relatively prime integers. Prove that if $f(r/s) = 0$ then s divides a_n and r divides a_0. Show that this implies that if $a_n = 1$ all rational roots of $f(x) = 0$ are integers.

13. Use the result of Exercise 12 to show

   a. There is no rational number whose square is 2. Compare Exercise 7.

   b. The number $\sqrt{2} + \sqrt{3}$ is not rational. HINT: Show that the given number is a root of an equation of the type described in Exercise 12.

14. Suppose, for integers a,b,c,d, we make the following definitions for the symbol (a/b):

   a. $(a/b) = (c/d)$ shall mean $a = c$, $b = d$.

   b. $(a/b) + (c/d) = (a + c/b + d)$.

   c. $(a/b)(c/d) = (ac - bd/ad + bc)$.

Show that this system has all the properties listed at the end of Section 1.2 for natural numbers.

1.11. Decimals and real numbers

As we all know, the decimal notation can be extended to represent certain fractions. For instance, we write 176.9304 to mean

$$1 \cdot 10^2 + 7 \cdot 10^1 + 6 \cdot 10^0 + 9 \cdot 10^{-1} + 3 \cdot 10^{-2} + 0 \cdot 10^{-3} + 4 \cdot 10^{-4}.$$

This means that only rational numbers which can be written in the form a/b, where b is a power of 10 and a is an integer, are exactly equal to a decimal. For instance, there is no decimal which is equal to 1/3, for if 1/3 were equal to $a/10^c$, where a is an integer prime to 10, we would have

$$3a = 10^c,$$

which is impossible, since 3 does not divide 10.

On the other hand, if our number system were to the base 3, 1/3 would be equal to a decimal,* whereas 1/10 could not.

---

* This probably would be called a "trimal."

However, the decimal may be used to approximate any rational number to any desired degree of accuracy; more precisely, for any positive rational number r and any small positive number e, we can find a decimal d such that $0 < r - d < e$. For instance,

$$1/3 - .3 = 1/30, 1/3 - .33 = 1/300, \cdots, 1/3 - .33 \cdots 3 = (1/3)10^{-k},$$

where in the last decimal there are k threes. Thus by choosing k to be 6, we can make the decimal closer to $1/3$ than 10^{-6}, and so forth.

This process of approximation works well when we are concerned with the decimal approximation of a rational number. However, if it is to be used to define new kinds of numbers, a slightly different point of view is necessary. If we write

$$d_k = .333 \cdots 3,$$

where there are k threes in the decimal, then the sequence

$$d_1, d_2, d_3, \cdots$$

may be said to define the number $1/3$ in the sense that $1/3$ is the smallest number which is not less than any d_k of the sequence. Consider the sequence of decimals:

$$(1) \qquad 1, 1.4, 1.41, 1.414, 1.4142, 1.41421, \cdots .$$

This is a sequence of rational numbers whose squares approach 2 from below. For instance, 1.414 is included because 1.414^2 is less than 2 and 1.415^2 is greater than 2. For the next entry we could compute 1.4141^2, 1.4142^2, 1.4143^2 and find that 2 lies between the second and third, hence list the second. By continuing far enough in the sequence, we can find a number whose square is as close as we please to 2.

Now, it is rather clear that the process just described yields a sequence of numbers having the property that by continuing far enough we can find a number of the sequence as close as we please to 2. (To paraphrase a once popular song: "No matter what you name, I can get closer.") This may be formally shown as follows. By our process, for any positive integer n, we find a number x_n of the sequence having the property that

$$x_n^2 < 2 < (x_n + 1/10^n)^2.$$

Since all the numbers involved are rational, we may use their properties to see that

$$2 - x_n^2 < (x_n + 1/10^n)^2 - x_n^2 = 2x_n/10^n + 1/10^{2n} < 5/10^n,$$

since x_n is less than 2 and $1/10^{2n} < 1/10^n$. This shows that by choosing n large enough we may make x_n^2 as close as we please to 2.

This sequence does not define a rational number in the sense that the decimal defines 1/3, for, as we now show, there is no smallest rational number greater than all the decimals of this sequence. To show this, suppose there were, and let it be designated by r. First, r^2 cannot be less than 2 because one of the sequences of decimals above (all of which are rational numbers) would have a square closer to 2 than r^2 and hence would be greater than r. Second, r^2 could not be greater than 2, for then one of the decimals

$$2, 1.5, 1.42, 1.415, 1.4143, 1.41422, \cdots$$

would be smaller than r and yet greater than all the decimals of (1); each such decimal of the above set is rational. This would contradict our assumption that r is the smallest. Finally, we have shown that $r^2 = 2$ is impossible if r is rational. Thus there are sequences of decimals of the form

$$(2) \qquad r, r.a_1, r.a_1a_2, r.a_1a_2a_3, \cdots,$$

where r is a natural number or 0 and each a_i is a digit, which do not define a rational number in the sense above. We then define a new kind of number called a **real number** as follows:

Definition: With every sequence of decimals of the form (2) we associate a real number R which, by definition, is considered to be so placed among the rational numbers that

1. R is greater than or equal to each number of the sequence.
2. If S is any rational number greater than or equal to every number of the sequence, then $S \geq R$.

Thus in this sense 1/3 is the real number defined by the sequence

$$.3, .33, .333, .3333, \cdots,$$

since it is greater than each number of the sequence; and if S is any rational number greater than or equal to each number of the sequence, $S \geq 1/3$.

On the other hand, there is no rational number defined by the sequence (1), and we designate by $\sqrt{2}$ the number defined by that sequence. A real number which is not rational we call an irrational number.

The term "real number" includes all rationals, for the decimal expansion of a rational number defines in this way the rational number. It includes integers, since 5 can be written $5.0000 \cdots$; and $2/5$, since it is $.40000 \cdots$. However, as we have seen, it also includes numbers which are not rational.

We have thus defined a real number to correspond with every sequence of decimals of the form (2). Is it possible for two sequences (2) to define the same real number? The answer is given in the following theorem which we shall prove.

Theorem 1.11. Two distinct sequences (2) define the same real number if and only if they are identical for the first k digits, k being some nonnegative integer, and from that point on, one has the sequence of digits $a000 \cdots$ and the other has the sequence $b999 \cdots$, where $a = b + 1$.

To simplify notation, first notice that if we have two decimal expansions, we may multiply or divide each by a large enough power of 10 to make the dissimilar portions begin immediately after the decimal point. (This is on the assumption that we may deal with real numbers as with rational ones.) Then, assuming the cancellation property for addition, the two numbers will be equal if and only if the dissimilar portions of their decimal expansions are equal. Thus we may consider our decimal expansions to be

$$S = .a_1a_2a_3 \cdots, \quad R = .b_1b_2b_3 \cdots.$$

We may, without loss of generality, assume $a_1 > b_1$.

First, if $a_1 \geq b_1 + 2$, then the rational number $c/10$, where $c = b_1 + 1$, will be greater than all decimals in the sequence for R. Hence $R \leq c$. However, c is less than all decimals in the sequence for S, a fact which shows that c cannot be S. Thus this case cannot happen.

Second, suppose $a_1 = b_1 + 1$. Then the rational number $a_1/10$ will be less than all the numbers in the sequence for S unless all a_i after the first are zero. On the other hand, if $b_2 \leq 8$, then the rational number $b_1/10 + 9/100$ will be greater than all the numbers in the sequence for R

and less than those for S. Notice that $a_1/10$ is greater than all the numbers of the sequence for S. Thus, if both sequences represent the same number, we must have $S = a_1/10$ and $b_2 = 9$. Repetition of this argument yields the desired result.

Since a decimal expansion can be obtained for π, it is a real number. Many equations have one or more real roots: $x^3 - 5 = 0$, $x^4 - x - 3 = 0$, and so forth.

Negative real numbers can be defined as we defined negative integers. It can be shown that they obey all the laws of the rational numbers, but we omit this because it is rather difficult.

1.12. Complex numbers

Though many equations have real roots, some have none. There is no decimal expansion of a root of $x^2 + 1 = 0$, since for x real the least value of x^2 is 0, and thus $x^2 + 1 \geq 1$. There can be no decimal whose square plus 1 is closer to 0 than 1. However, mathematicians are insatiable, and they have created a number whose square is -1 and call it $\sqrt{-1}$ or i. By definition, $i^2 = -1$. Any number of the form $a + bi$ where a and b are real numbers is called a **complex number**. If $b \neq 0$, it is called **imaginary**; if $a = 0 \neq b$, it is called **pure imaginary**. Furthermore, we define $a + bi = c + di$ if $a = c$, $b = d$, for a,b,c,d real, and we define addition and multiplication by

$$(a + bi) + (c + di) = (a + c) + (b + d)i$$
$$(a + bi)(c + di) = ac + adi + bci + bdi^2 = (ac - bd) + (ad + bc)i.$$

These numbers have all the fundamental properties of the rational numbers.

It is a remarkable fact that any polynomial in x with complex coefficients is equal to a product of factors of the form $x - c$ where c is a complex number, that is, any polynomial

$$a_n x^n + a_{n-1} x^{n-1} + a_{n-2} x^{n-2} + \cdots + a_1 x + a_0, \ a_n \neq 0,$$

where a_i are complex numbers, can be expressed in the form

$$a_n(x - c_1)(x - c_2) \cdots (x - c_n),$$

where the c_i are complex numbers. Hence we have reached the end of the road as far as solutions of equations are concerned; we need no new kinds of numbers to express the roots of any equation whose coefficients are numbers of the kinds already discussed.

To recapitulate: We started with the natural numbers and could not solve the equation $a + x = b$, when a and b are natural numbers and a is greater than b. Hence we invented negative integers and then could solve all such equations where a and b are integers, positive or negative. However, with integers alone, we could not solve $ax = b$ where b is not a multiple of a. Thus we invented rational numbers so that every equation $ax = b$, where a and b are integers and $a \neq 0$, is solvable. As it happened, all such equations where a and b are rational numbers are also solvable in rational numbers.

However, $x^2 - 2 = 0$ is not solvable in rational numbers, a highly unsatisfactory state of affairs, which bothered the Greeks very much over two thousand years ago. Therefore, we invented the real numbers and saw that this equation had real roots. Since $x^2 + 1 = 0$ has no real roots, we invented imaginary and complex numbers, and the process is complete, as indicated above. For this reason, the set of complex numbers is sometimes called complete, since it includes real numbers, rational numbers, and, in fact, all the numbers of this chapter.

Exercises 1.12

1. Classify each of the following as being a natural number, integer, rational number, irrational number, real number, complex number, and imaginary number:

$$5, \; -8, \; -5/4, \; \sqrt{2}/\sqrt{8}, \; \sqrt{4}, \; 6, \text{ roots of } x^2 - 7 = 0, \text{ roots of } x^2 + 5 = 0,$$
$$\pi, \; \sin 45^0.$$

2. Are the sum and product of two rational numbers necessarily rational? Are the sum and product of two irrational numbers necessarily irrational?

3. Is the sum of a rational number and an irrational number ever rational? Is the product of a rational number and an irrational number ever rational?

4. If $a + br = c + dr$, where $a,b,c,$ and d are rational numbers and r irrational, show that $a = c$ and $b = d$.

5. Answer Questions 2, 3, 4 with "rational" and "irrational" replaced by "real" and "imaginary."

6. Suppose we defined $a + bi > c + di$ if $a > c$ or $a = c$ and $b > d$, with a,b,c,d real numbers. If x,y, and z are three complex numbers, which of the following properties of inequalities would hold?

  a. $x > y, y > z$ implies $x > z$.
  b. $x > 0, y > z$ implies $xy > xz$.

7. Show that there is a complex number satisfying the equation $x^2 + i = 0$ where $i = \sqrt{-1}$.

8. Find the decimal expansions for each of the following rational numbers, and notice what properties they have in common:

$$1/3, \ 1/5, \ 1/7, \ 1/11, \ 1/13, \ 2/7, \ 3/7, \ 11/7, \ 1/17.$$

Can you prove any of these properties? Keep these results on hand for reference in the following chapter.

9. If the symbol (a/b) in Exercise 14 of Section 1.10 is identified with $a + bi$, show that

  a. $(a/b) + (c/d)$ as defined is identified with $(a + bi) + (c + di)$.
  b. $(a/b)(a/d)$ is identified with $(a + bi)(c + di)$.

Repeating Decimals and Congruences

2.1. Repeating decimals

We shall begin by exploring certain interesting properties of decimals, and in the process develop certain fundamentals of the theory of numbers which not only serve to explain these properties but are also useful in many other connections. A repeating or periodic decimal (Ref. 1) is one in which the same sequence of digits recurs and continues to recur from a certain point on. Some examples are

$$.1212121212 \cdots \; ; 3.4156156156 \cdots \; ; 2.30000 \cdots ,$$

where we have underlined the recurring portion which we shall call the repetend. Every repeating decimal may be expressed as the quotient of two integers, that is, a rational number. This may easily be seen from two examples:

EXAMPLE 1. To find the rational number n equal to $4.123123123 \cdots$, see that $1000n = 4123.123123 \cdots$ and hence that $1000n - n = 4123.0 - 4 = 4119$. Hence $999n = 4119$, and $n = 4119/999$.

EXAMPLE 2. $n = 412.3412341234 \cdots$. Then $10000n - n = 4123000$, which implies that $n = 4123000/9999$. What is the relationship between the power of 10 by which n is multiplied and the repeating decimal?

To prove formally that every repeating decimal may be expressed as the quotient of two integers, let N be any repeating decimal. By multiplying N by 10^k, for k an integer (not necessarily positive), we may make $10^k N$, which we denote by M, have the property that its repetend begins immediately after the decimal point. Thus we may write M in the form

$$M = a + b \cdot 10^{-n} + b \cdot 10^{-2n} + b \cdot 10^{-3n} + \cdots ,$$

where n is the number of digits in the repetend and b is the repetend. Then

$$10^n \cdot M = a \cdot 10^n + b + b \cdot 10^{-n} + b \cdot 10^{-2n} + \cdots ,$$
$$M = \qquad a + b \cdot 10^{-n} + b \cdot 10^{-2n} + \cdots .$$

Subtraction gives

$$(10^n - 1)M = 10^n a + b - a,$$

and hence M is the rational number

$$\frac{10^n a + b - a}{10^n - 1} = a + \frac{b}{10^n - 1}.$$

Thus N is 10^{-k} multiplied by the value above for M.

Conversely, it is true that the decimal expansion of any rational number is repeating if, as above, we call a terminating decimal "repeating" in the sense that 0 recurs in the expansion. See Exercise 2, below.

A short table of repetends

$1/7 = .142857 \cdots$

$1/13 = .076923 \cdots$

$1/19 = .05263\ 15789\ 47368\ 421 \cdots$

$1/17 = .05882\ 35294\ 11764\ 7 \cdots$

$1/23 = .04347\ 82608\ 69565\ 21739\ 13 \cdots$

$1/29 = .03448\ 27586\ 20689\ 65517\ 24137\ 931 \cdots$

$1/31 = .03225\ 80645\ 16129 \cdots$

$1/37 = .027 \cdots$

Exercises 2.1

1. Find the rational number equal to $31.2145145 \cdots$.

2. If in a process of division a remainder appears which appeared before, why must the expansion repeat from that point on? Why in dividing one integer by another must eventually a remainder appear which occurred before? How may this be used to show that any rational number has a repeating decimal?

3. Use the development in Exercise 2 above to show that the number of digits in the repeating part of the decimal expansion of a/b cannot exceed $b - 1$.

4. Show that the repetend of the decimal expansion for $1/m$ for any integer m occurs between the first two times that the remainder is 1 in the division, if m is prime to 10.

5. Show that the results of the above exercise hold also if 1 is replaced by r, a positive integer less than m, and hence that any such decimal repeats from the beginning.

6. Compare the decimal expansions of each of the following sets:

$$1/3 \, , 1/13 \, , 1/23 \; ; 1/7 \, , 1/17 \, , 1/37 \; ;$$
$$1/9 \, , 1/19 \, , 1/29 \, .$$

7. Each of the following letters represents a digit chosen from 0 to 9 inclusive, and no two letters represent the same digit. A fraction, equal to a repeating decimal, is indicated. Find what values the letters must have:

$$\frac{EVE}{DID} = .TALKTALK \cdots .$$

2.2. Number of terms in the repetend of the repeating decimal

The student's experience with the previous exercises shows that when a remainder recurs, the decimal expansion repeats. For instance, in the division of 11 by 7, the first and seventh remainders are 4, and the repetend begins with the second digit of the expansion and ends with the seventh. In the expansion of 3/7, the first and seventh remainders are 2, and the repetend consists of the first six terms of the expansion. This must be so, in general, since what follows any point in the division depends only on the remainder at that point. Furthermore, division by a number b can yield at most $b - 1$ different remainders. Hence, if the first $b - 1$ remainders are distinct, the next one must have occurred before. This shows that the repetend of the decimal expansion of a/b can contain no more than $b - 1$ digits.

The above result can be seen more clearly if we notice that the first remainder in the decimal expansion of $1/7$ is the remainder when 10 is divided by 7, the second remainder when 10^2 is divided by 7, and the nth remainder when 10^n is divided by 7. Similarly, in the expansion of $11/7$,

the successive remainders in the division process are the remainders of
11, $11 \cdot 10$, $11 \cdot 10^2$, $11 \cdot 10^3$, and so forth, when divided by 7. There cannot
be any more than six different remainders.

2.3. Congruence notation

There is a convenient notation due to Gauss (one of the greatest
mathematicians of all times), which is of assistance in the above descrip-
tion (Ref. 11, pp. 209 ff.). Instead of saying that 3 is the remainder
when 10 is divided by 7, 2 when 10^2 is divided by 7, and the like, we write

$$10 \equiv 3 \pmod{7} , \; 10^2 \equiv 2 \pmod{7} , \; 10^3 \equiv 6 \pmod{7}.$$

In general,

$$a \equiv b \pmod{m} \text{ means } a - b \text{ is divisible by } m.$$

It is read: a is congruent to b mod m (mod being short for "modulo").
Hence 100 is congruent not only to 2 (mod 7) but to 9, 16, 30, -5, etc.

Thus we could express the results in the last part of Section 2 as
follows: The remainders in the division of 1 by 7 are the numbers congruent to 10, 10^2, 10^3, and so forth (mod 7); the remainders in the division of
11 by 7 are the numbers congruent to 11 times 10, 10^2, 10^3, and so forth
(mod 7). In general, if we divide a by b, the remainders in the process are
those numbers congruent to a times the powers of 10 (mod b).

Another meaning which could be ascribed to the symbol

$$a \equiv b \pmod{m}$$

would be as follows: The remainders when a and b are divided by m are
the same. That this is equivalent to the former meaning can be shown
as follows. Suppose $a = mq + r, b = ms + t$, where r and t are nonnegative
integers less than m; that is, r and t are the remainders when a and b are
divided by m. Then $a - b - m(q - s) = r - t$, and, if $a - b$ is divisible
by m, then $r - t$ is also; and since r and t are less than m,

$$|r - t| < m,$$

which * shows that $r - t = 0$ or $r = t$. On the other hand, if $r = t$, we would
have $a - b = mq - ms$, which is divisible by m.

---

* The absolute value of a number b is written $|b|$ and means the number $-b$ if b is
negative, and $+b$ if b is positive or zero.

In brief, we have just shown that if the difference of two numbers is divisible by m their remainders when divided by m are the same and conversely.

Exercises 2.3

1. Use the congruence notation to find the first three remainders in the division of 11 by 21.

2. Prove that if $a \cdot 10^r \equiv a \cdot 10^s$ (mod 7), where $r > s$, then $a \cdot 10^{r-s} \equiv a$ (mod 7). What does this show about the repetition in the expansion of $a/7$?

3. If the number 7 in Exercise 2 were replaced by 11, would the same result hold? What if 7 were replaced by 15? What general conclusions could you draw for 7 replaced by any integer b?

4. Which of the following properties of congruences hold? Specify any exceptions.

   a. $a \equiv b$ (mod m) implies $ac \equiv bc$ (mod m).
   b. $ar \equiv br$ (mod m) implies $a \equiv b$ (mod m). (Compare Exercise 3.)
   c. $a \equiv b$ (mod m) implies $a + c \equiv b + c$ (mod m).
   d. $a \equiv b$ (mod m), $c \equiv d$ (mod m) implies $ac \equiv bd$ (mod m).

5. If $a^r \equiv b$ (mod m), prove that $a^{rs} \equiv b^s$ (mod m). Use this to find the remainder when 3^{40} is divided by 10, that is, the last digit in 3^{40}. What is the last digit in 7^{20}?

2.4. Properties of congruences

In Exercise 4 above you were asked to examine the truth of

Theorem 2.4a. If $a \equiv b$ (mod m), then $ac \equiv bc$ (mod m).

This is true, since $a - b$ divisible by m implies $(a - b)c$ is divisible by m and hence $ac - bc$ is also.

You were also asked to test the truth of

Theorem 2.4b. If $a \equiv b$ (mod m), then $a + c \equiv b + c$ (mod m). This is true, since $a - b = a + c - (b + c)$ implies that if one difference is divisible by m the other is.

On the other hand, $ar \equiv br$ (mod m) does not always imply that $a \equiv b$ (mod m), as is shown by the fact that $6 \equiv 27$ (mod 21) but $2 \not\equiv 9$ (mod 21). Suppose $ar - br$ is divisible by m. Then $(a - b)r$ is divisible by m; that is, m must be the product of two factors one of which divides r and the other $a - b$. Let d be the largest factor of m which divides r; that is, let d be the g.c.d. of m and r. Then $r(a - b)$ divisible by m implies $(a - b)(r/d)$ is divisible by m/d. However, r/d and m/d have no common factor greater than 1, since if q were such a factor, m and r would have the common factor dq which is larger than d. Hence m/d divides $a - b$, and we have proved

Theorem 2.4c. If $ar \equiv br$ (mod m) and d is the g.c.d. of m and r, then $a \equiv b$ (mod m/d).

We leave to the student the proof of

Theorem 2.4d. If $f(x)$ is a polynomial in x with integer coefficients, then $a \equiv b$ (mod m) implies that $f(a) \equiv f(b)$ (mod m).

Congruence is a kind of equality in that it has the properties of equality given in Section 1.2 (see Exercise 13 below). Theorems 2.4a and 2.4b show that multiplication and addition are well defined relative to congruence. From this point of view congruence (mod m) can be thought of as a separation of all the integers into classes, each class containing all the numbers congruent to each other (mod m). For instance, if our modulus is 3, the integers are divided into three classes as follows:

$$\begin{array}{ll} \text{Class of 0:} & -9\,,\,-6\,,\,-3\,,\,0\,,\,3\,,\,6\,,\,\ 9\,,\,\cdots\,; \\ \text{Class of 1:} & -8\,,\,-5\,,\,-2\,,\,1\,,\,4\,,\,7\,,\,10\,,\,\cdots\,; \\ \text{Class of 2:} & -7\,,\,-4\,,\,-1\,,\,2\,,\,5\,,\,8\,,\,11\,,\,\cdots\,. \end{array}$$

In the sense of congruence, any number of one class is "equal" to any other number of that class. From this point of view, adding 7 and 4 is the same as adding 1 and 1 or -5 and -2, since all three sums are in the class of -1. Similarly, $7 \cdot 8 \equiv 2$ (mod 3), since $1 \cdot 2 \equiv 2$ (mod 3).

For ease of reference we exhibit below the addition and multiplication tables of integers mod 7.

Addition (mod 7)

	1	2	3	4	5	6
1	2	3	4	5	6	0
2	3	4	5	6	0	1
3	4	5	6	0	1	2
4	5	6	0	1	2	3
5	6	0	1	2	3	4
6	0	1	2	3	4	5

Multiplication (mod 7)

	1	2	3	4	5	6
1	1	2	3	4	5	6
2	2	4	6	1	3	5
3	3	6	2	5	1	4
4	4	1	5	2	6	3
5	5	3	1	6	4	2
6	6	5	4	3	2	1

Exercises 2.4

1. Write out the addition and multiplication tables mod 11 and mod 12.

2. What properties do the tables mod 7, mod 11, and mod 12 have? Can you prove any of them for a general modulus m?

3. Use the tables to solve each of the following equations, when solutions exist, for $b = 7, 11, 12$.

    a. $5 + x \equiv 3 \pmod{b}$.
    b. $5x \equiv 13 \pmod{b}$.
    c. $4x \equiv 13 \pmod{b}$.

Where a congruence is not solvable, give reasons for the lack of solution.

4. Judging from your experience in solving the equations above, what would you guess to be the condition in order that each of the following congruences be solvable?

    a. $a + x \equiv b \pmod{m}$.
    b. $ax \equiv b \pmod{m}$.

Go as far as you can in proving your conjecture.

5. Given $x \equiv m \pmod{a}$, $x \equiv m \pmod{b}$, show that $(a,b) = 1$ implies $x \equiv m \pmod{ab}$. What would your conclusion be if $(a,b) = d > 1$?

6. If $ab \equiv 1 \pmod{m}$ and $bx \equiv c \pmod{m}$, show that $x \equiv ac \pmod{m}$ and hence a could be called the reciprocal of $b \pmod{m}$.

7. Show that $a_n 10^n + a_{n-1} 10^{n-1} + \cdots + a_1 10 + a_0$, where the a_i's are integers, is congruent to $a_n + a_{n-1} + \cdots + a_1 + a_0 \pmod{9}$ and hence that any number is congruent (mod 9), to the sum of its digits. How would you express this without the use of the notion of congruence?

8. How would you perform the following trick? You ask a friend to "think of a number" and then form another number by mixing the digits. He then is to subtract the smaller from the larger and tell you all but one of the digits in the difference. You then tell him the missing one. For instance, he may choose 57689; he scrambles the digits to get 98567 and subtracts, getting 40878. He tells you of the digits 0,4,8, and 8, and you inform him that the other one is 7.

9. Find an expression in $a_n, a_{n-1}, \cdots, a_1, a_0$ to which

$$a_n 10^n + a_{n-1} 10^{n-1} + \cdots + a_1 10 + a_0$$

is congruent (mod 11). Is there for this result an analogue to the trick in Exercise 8? (For other tests of divisibility, see Ref. 9.)

10. If N is a two-digit number and M the number obtained from N by interchanging the digits, show that $N - M$ is divisible by 9. Find all such numbers N for which $N - M = 27$.

11. Show that $(x + y)^p \equiv x^p + y^p \pmod{p}$, where p is a prime number.

12. Prove Theorem 2.4d.

13. Prove that congruence has the four properties of equalities given in Section 1.2.

14. Teams A and B contain six men each. How does the multiplication table (mod 7) give a plan by which each man of team A plays each man of team B, six matches being played simultaneously?

15. Prove that a number which is a square must have one of the following as its last digit: 0,1,4,5,6,9. What can you say of the last two digits?

2.5. Congruential equations

It is easy to show that the congruence $a + x \equiv b \pmod{m}$ is always solvable, since $b + a = x$ is a solution. We partially prove

Theorem 2.5a. The congruence $ax \equiv b \pmod{m}$ is solvable if the g.c.d. of a and m is 1, and then there is only one solution (mod m).

We give the proof for m a prime number p and leave to the reader the proof for m composite. Let a be an integer not divisible by p and write the numbers

$$(1) \qquad\qquad a, 2a, 3a, \cdots, (p-1)a, pa.$$

No two of them are congruent (mod p), since $xa \equiv ya$ (mod p) would imply $x \equiv y$ (mod p) by Theorem 2.4c. However, there are p of them, and thus p classes represented. Hence, since there are only p classes (mod p), one of them must be the class of b; that is, b must be congruent (mod p) to one of the numbers (1).

Notice that Theorem 2.5a implies that $ax \equiv 1$ (mod m) is solvable if and only if $(a,m) = 1$. When this congruence has a solution b, then b is essentially the reciprocal of a, and to solve the congruence

$$ax \equiv c \text{ (mod } m)$$

we need merely multiply by b and have $abx \equiv x \equiv bc$ (mod m), as was seen in Exercise 6 above.

Another consequence of Theorem 2.5a is

Theorem 2.5b. The congruence $ax \equiv b$ (mod m) is solvable if and only if the g.c.d. of a and m divides b. If it is solvable there are (a,m) distinct solutions.

To prove this, suppose $ar \equiv b$ (mod m); then $ar - b$ is divisible by m, and any factor common to a and m would have to divide b. Suppose $(a,m) = g$ and $g|b$. Then $ax \equiv b$ (mod m) if and only if

$$(a/g)x \equiv b/g \text{ (mod } m/g).$$

Since $(a/g, m/g) = 1$, this has just one solution (mod m/g), and if this solution is x_0, then the solutions of the congruence $ax \equiv b$ (mod m) are

$$x_0, x_0 + m/g, x_0 + 2m/g, \cdots, x_0 + (g-1)m/g.$$

There are better ways of solving a congruential equation than that suggested by the proof, but it does supply a definite way of finding a solution of such a congruence. The reader should apply this method to the solution of the congruences in Exercise 3b and 3c above.

A similar method of proof may be used to give the following useful result sometimes referred to as Fermat's Little Theorem (Ref. 11, pp. 54 ff.).

Theorem 2.5c. If a is not divisible by a prime number p, then

$$a^{p-1} \equiv 1 \text{ (mod } p).$$

To prove this, consider the set of numbers in (2.5), omitting pa from the list. The set is then congruent to $1,2,3,\cdots, p - 1$ in some order, and hence the product of the numbers of the set is congruent to $(p - 1)!$ (mod p). Thus we have

$$a^{p-1}(p - 1)! \equiv (p - 1)! \pmod{p}.$$

Since $(p - 1)!$ is not divisible by p, Theorem 2.4c shows us that we may divide by the factorial $p - 1$ to get our desired result.

This theorem of Fermat establishes a property of the repeating part of the decimal expansion of $1/p$ when p is a prime number not dividing 10, for we have

$$10^{p-1} \equiv 1 \pmod{p},$$

which means that in the division of 1 by p, the $(p - 1)^{st}$ remainder is 1. Furthermore, the $(p - 1)^{st}$ remainder in the division of a/p is the same as the remainder when a is divided by p.

Exercises 2.5

1. Use the method of proof of Theorem 2.5a to solve the congruence $5x \equiv 3 \pmod{11}$.

2. Prove that the number of terms in the repetend of the decimal expansion for a/p, where p does not divide a, is a divisor of $p - 1$, p being a prime number.

3. Prove that for every prime number p, except 2 and 5, there is a multiple p whose every digit is 9.

4. If $(10^n - 1)/p$ is a positive integer, what is its last digit if $p \equiv 1$ (mod 10)? If $p \equiv 3 \pmod{10}$? If $p \equiv 7 \pmod{10}$? If $p \equiv 9 \pmod{10}$?

5. Prove Fermat's Theorem by showing that

$$(1 + 1 + \cdots + 1)^p \equiv (1 + 1 + \cdots + 1) \pmod{p},$$

where the number of 1's is less than p.

6. Prove that $a^p \equiv a \pmod{p}$ for p a prime number.

7. Prove that if $m^p + n^p \equiv 0 \pmod{p}$ then $m^p + n^p \equiv 0 \pmod{p^2}$ for p an odd prime number. (Ref. 3, p. 50.)

8. State and prove the theorem corresponding to Fermat's Little Theorem for a composite number m instead of p. (In the proof, replace the set $1, 2, 3, \cdots, p - 1$ by the positive numbers less than m and prime to m.) What are the consequences of this theorem in connection with the decimal expansion of a/m, where m is a composite number not divisible by 5 or 2? Why is the last restriction necessary?

9. Let x and y each take the following $(m + 1)/2$ values:

$$0, 1, 2, 3, \cdots, (m - 1)/2,$$

where m is an odd integer. If a is an integer, show that no two of the resulting $(m + 1)/2$ values of $x + a$ are equal. Since $(m + 1)/2 + (m + 1)/2 = m + 1$ and there are only m different numbers (mod m), show that at least one value of $x + a$ is congruent to one value of y and hence that

$$x + a \equiv y \pmod{m}$$

has a solution x, y for which $0 \le x < m/2$ and $0 \le y < m/2$.

10. Using the same principle as in Exercise 9, show that

$$ax \equiv y \pmod{p}$$

has a nontrivial solution in integers x and y less in absolute value than $\sqrt{p}$ for p, a prime not dividing a.

11. Can Exercise 10 be extended for p, a composite number?

12. Does $a^2 \equiv b^2 \pmod{m}$ imply $a \equiv b \pmod{m}$ or $a \equiv -b \pmod{m}$? What is your answer if m is a prime or a power of a prime?

2.6. The Euler Phi-function

An important number theoretic function is the so-called Euler Phi-function defined as follows: $\phi(1) = 1$ and, if $m > 1$, $\phi(m)$ is defined to be the number of positive integers less than m and prime to m. For instance, $\phi(12) = 4$, since $1, 5, 7, 11$ are the positive integers less than 12 and prime to 12. A theorem for composite numbers analogous to Theorem 2.5c is known as Euler's Theorem and may be stated as follows:

Theorem 2.6a. If $(a, m) = 1$, then $a^{\phi(m)} \equiv 1 \pmod{m}$.

To prove this, we let

$$(1) \qquad\qquad\qquad a_1, a_2, \cdots, a_t,$$

where $t = \phi(m)$, be the positive integers less than m and having no factors in common with m, in other words, the positive integers less than m and prime to m. If a is any number prime to m, as in the proof of Theorem 2.5a, we see that

$$aa_1, aa_2, \cdots, aa_t$$

are all prime to m and no two are congruent (mod m). Hence they are congruent in some order to the numbers of (1). Taking the product of both sets, we have

$$a^t(a_1a_2 \cdots a_t) \equiv a_1a_2 \cdots a_t \ (\text{mod } m),$$

and, dividing both sides by the product of the a's, we have our theorem.

The a's in (1) constitute what we call a **reduced residue system** (mod m); in fact, a reduced residue system is any set of $\phi(m)$ numbers congruent to the numbers of (1). Similarly, any set of m numbers incongruent (mod m) we call a **complete residue system** (mod m).

A generalization of the result in Exercise 2, above, is a direct consequence of

Theorem 2.6b. If a is prime to m and r is the least positive exponent for which $a^r \equiv 1 \ (\text{mod } m)$ and if $a^s \equiv 1 \ (\text{mod } m)$, then r divides s.

To prove this, suppose we write out the powers of a (mod m). The first r powers are distinct (mod m), since $a^t \equiv a^u \ (\text{mod } m)$ with $r > t > u$ would imply $a^{t-u} \equiv 1 \ (\text{mod } m)$ and $t - u$ would be positive and less than r, contrary to the assumption about r.

Hence the powers of a may be written in rows as follows:

$$a, a^2, a^3, \cdots, a^r \equiv 1,$$
$$a^{r+1}, a^{r+2}, \cdots, a^{2r} \equiv 1,$$
$$a^{2r+1}, a^{2r+2}, \cdots, a^{3r} \equiv 1,$$

$$\cdot \quad \cdot \quad \cdot \quad \cdot \quad \cdot \quad \cdot \quad \cdot \quad \cdot \quad \cdot \quad \cdot ,$$

where only the last power in each row is congruent to 1 (mod m). If, then, $a^s \equiv 1 \ (\text{mod } m)$, it must occur at the end of one of the rows and hence must be an integral multiple of r. This proves our theorem. In view of Euler's Theorem we have

Corollary 2.6b. If r is the least positive exponent for which $a^r \equiv 1$ (mod m), then r is a divisor of $\phi(m)$. We call r the **exponent to which** a

belongs (mod m). This immediately implies that in any decimal expansion of a/m, where m is prime to 10, the number of digits in the repetend is a divisor of $\phi(m)$.

2.7. Factorization by means of Euler's Theorem

Certain types of numbers may be factored easily by use of Euler's Theorem and the properties of congruences. Suppose we seek the divisors of $n = 5^7 - 1$. From Theorem 2.6b we know that if r is the least exponent of 5 such that $5^r \equiv 1$ (mod p), for any prime p dividing n, then r must divide 7 since $5^7 \equiv 1$ (mod p).

Now, $r = 1$ would imply $5 - 1 \equiv 0$ (mod p) and hence $p = 2$. In that case, $5^7 - 1 = (5^2)^3 5 - 1 \equiv 1^3 \cdot 5 - 1 \equiv 5 - 1 \equiv 4$ (mod 8). Thus, if $p \neq 2$, r must be different from 1 and a divisor of 7, hence $r = 7$. Hence by Corollary 2.6b the only prime divisors of n beside 2 are primes p for which

$$p - 1 \equiv 0 \ (\text{mod } 7);$$

that is, primes $p \equiv 1$ (mod 7). However, p is odd and therefore must be 1 more than an *even* multiple of 7; that is,

$$p \equiv 1 \ (\text{mod } 14).$$

If $n/4$ has a prime factor p less than $n/4$ it must have one not greater than $\sqrt{n}/2$ because certainly p, a factor, implies that either p or $n/4p$ is not greater than $\sqrt{n}/2$. Thus the only possible primes which need to be tried are those less than 139 and congruent to 1 (mod 14). These primes are

$$29, 43, 71, 113.$$

Now $5^7 \equiv (-4)^3 \cdot 5 \equiv -64 \cdot 5 \equiv -30 \equiv -1$ (mod 29). Similar computation shows that n is not divisible by 43, 71, or 113, and hence that $n/4$ is a prime number.

A slight variation of method enables us to consider $n = 5^7 + 1$. A little computation shows that $n \equiv 2$ (mod 4), n is divisible by 3 but not by 9 and, by the above, $n \equiv 0$ (mod 29). Dividing n by $2 \cdot 3 \cdot 29$ gives 449, which is a prime number.

2.8. Further properties of repeating decimals

Consider the repetend occurring in the decimal expansion of $1/7$, namely, 142857. If we multiply this number by 3 we get 428571, by 2 we get 285714, and so on. For every multiplier from 1 to 6 we get a so-called **cyclic permutation** of the digits of the original repetend; that is, if we write two repetends in succession:

$$142857142857,$$

multiplication by 3 gives us the number formed by the six digits beginning with the 4, multiplication by 2 gives the number composed of the six digits beginning with the 2, and so on. One may also accomplish the same result by writing the digits of the repetend in order around a circle; hence the term **cyclic**. Similarly, if we multiply the repetend of the expansion of $1/17$ by the numbers from 1 to 16, we would have the sixteen cyclic permutations of the digits in the repetend. Why is this so? Can the same conclusion be drawn for 19,23,13,31,37? If so, why; if not, what can be said? (For example, if we multiply the repetend for $1/19$ by the numbers from 1 to 18, do we get the eighteen cyclic permutations?)

There is another rather remarkable property of such repetends. For instance, the sixteen digits in the repetend of $1/17$ are the digits from 0 to 9, inclusive and, in addition, the six which occur in the repetend of $1/7$. The repetend of $1/47$ has 46 digits which consist of four sets of 0 to 9 and the six which occur in the repetend of $1/7$. Suppose we have any prime p whose last digit is 7 and whose repetend N contains $p - 1$ digits. If we multiply N by the numbers from 1 to $p - 1$ in succession, each digit occurring in N will be transferred once and only once to the right end of the number. Hence the digits in N will be just those that occur at the right end of the numbers cN for $c = 1,2, \cdots, p - 1$. The last digit in N will be 7 (see Exercise 4 of Section 2.5). If we multiply N by the numbers from 1 to 10, inclusive, the last digits will be congruent to $7c$ (mod 10) for $c = 1,2, \cdots, 10$ and hence will be the numbers $0,1, \cdots, 9$ in some order. This will be true for each interval of 10 less than p. This accounts for the sets of numbers 0 to 9 in N. The remaining six digits will be obtained by multiplying N by $p - 1$, $p - 2$, $p - 3$, $p - 4$, $p - 5$, $p - 6$, whose last digits are 6,5,4,3,2,1, respectively; and $N \equiv 7$ (mod 10) shows that the products are congruent, respectively, to 2,5,8,1,4,7, which are the digits occurring in the repetend of $1/7$.

2.9. Properties of the Euler Phi-function

Recall that if the g.c.d. of b and c is g we write $(b,c) = g$.   And if $(b,c) = 1$, we call b and c relatively prime.   There is a rather simple formula for $\phi(m)$ for any integer m which may be obtained easily once we have proved

Theorem 2.9. If b and c are relatively prime integers, $\phi(bc) = \phi(b)\phi(c)$.

To prove this, let $b_1, b_2, \cdots, b_r$ be a reduced residue system (mod b), and let $c_1, c_2, \cdots, c_s$ be a reduced set (mod c).

The congruence

$$bx + b_1 \equiv c_j \pmod{c}$$

has a solution x_{1j} for each c_j, $j = 1, 2, \cdots, s$, since $(b,c) = 1$.

Thus

(1) $$bx_{11} + b_1, \, bx_{12} + b_1, \, bx_{13} + b_1, \, \cdots, \, bx_{1s} + b_1$$

are all congruent to b_1 (mod b) and congruent in order to $c_1, c_2, \cdots, c_s$ (mod c).

The congruence

$$bx + b_2 \equiv c_j \pmod{c}$$

has a solution x_{2j} for each value of c_j and the members of the set

(2) $$bx_{21} + b_2, \, bx_{22} + b_2, \, \cdots, \, bx_{2s} + b_2$$

are all congruent to b_2 (mod b) and congruent in order to $c_1, c_2, \cdots, c_s$ (mod c).   Thus for each b_i there will be a set of s numbers congruent to b_i (mod b) and congruent in order to $c_1, c_2, \cdots, c_s$ (mod c).   Each of these is prime to b and c and hence to bc; no two are congruent both (mod b) and (mod c); and hence no two are congruent (mod bc), and there are rs of them.   Furthermore, every number prime to bc must be congruent to one of the b_i (mod b) and one of the c_j (mod c) and hence is one of the rs numbers.

We have thus shown the existence of a set of rs numbers having the following properties:

1. All are prime to bc.
2. No two are congruent (mod bc).
3. Every number prime to bc is congruent to one of the set.

Thus, each positive number less than bc and prime to bc is congruent (mod bc) to just one of the set, and hence, there are exactly rs such numbers. This completes the proof.

Let m be expressed as a product of powers of distinct primes as follows:

$$m = p_1^{a_1} p_2^{a_2} \cdots p_r^{a_r}.$$

Theorem 2.9 then shows us that $\phi(m) = \phi(p_1^{a_1})\phi(p_2^{a_2}) \cdots \phi(p_r^{a_r})$, which, by Exercise 4 below, is

$$(p_1^{a_1} - p_1^{a_1-1})(p_2^{a_2} - p_2^{a_2-1}) \cdots (p_r^{a_r} - p_r^{a_r-1})$$

and which may be written $\phi(m) = m(1 - 1/p_1)(1 - 1/p_2) \cdots (1 - 1/p_r)$.

Exercises 2.9

1. For what numbers m is $\phi(m)$ odd? When is $\phi(m) = m/2$?

2. Prove that if r is the least value of x for which $a^x \equiv b^x \pmod{m}$, where a and b are prime to m, then $a^y \equiv b^y \pmod{m}$ implies that y is divisible by r.

3. Prove that if r is the least value of x for which $a^x \equiv -1 \pmod{m}$ and if $a^y \equiv 1 \pmod{m}$ then $2r$ divides y.

4. Prove that if p is a prime number, $\phi(p^n) = p^n - p^{n-1}$.

5. Show that $2^p - 1$ is prime for $p = 13$ and composite for $p = 11$ and 23.

6. Show that $2^{16} + 1$ is a prime number.

7. If p is a prime whose last digit is 3 and if the repetend of $1/p$ contains $p - 1$ digits, what can be said about the digits in the repetend (see Section 2.8)? What is the case for p whose last digit is 1 or 9?

8. The repetend of 13 contains only 6 digits. Can the above results be extended to such a case?

9. If $a_1, a_2, \cdots, a_t$ is a reduced residue system (mod m), show that ba_1, $ba_2, \cdots, ba_t$ is a reduced system if $(m,b) = 1$.

10. Show that $x^{17} - x \equiv 0 \pmod{15 \cdot 17 \cdot 32}$ for all odd integers x.

11. What is the largest number m you can find such that $x^{19} - x \equiv 0 \pmod{m}$ for all x?

12. Show that the number of positive fractions in lowest terms between 0 and 1 and whose denominators are not greater than n is

$$\phi(1) + \phi(2) + \cdots + \phi(n).$$

13. Write the numbers $bx + b_i$ in the proof of Theorem 2.9 for $b = 5$ and $c = 3$.

14. If $b_1, b_2, \cdots, b_t$ constitute a reduced residue system (mod b) and $c_1, c_2, \cdots, c_s$ a reduced system (mod c), prove that every number d in the reduced system (mod bc) is congruent to some b_i (mod b) and some c_j (mod c). Prove that any number d congruent to some b_i (mod b) and some c_j (mod c) is in a reduced residue system (mod bc). How may this be used to prove Theorem 2.9?

15. Prove that the sum of the numbers of a reduced residue system (mod m) is divisible by m if $m > 2$.

16. Answer the questions in the first paragraph of Section 2.8.

17. If r is the least power of a such that $a^r \equiv 1$ (mod p) and $(s,r) = 1$, show that r is the least power of a^s such that $(a^s)^r \equiv 1$ (mod p).

2.10.   Multiplicative functions

The Euler ϕ-function is called a **multiplicative function**, since $(b,c) = 1$ implies $\phi(bc) = \phi(b)\phi(c)$. There are various number-theoretic functions having this property. Two such functions are $\sigma(n)$, the sum of the divisors of n, and $d(n)$, the number of divisors of n (see Exercises 9 and 10 after Section 2.13).

Recalling that $d|n$ means "d divides n," we prove a general theorem on multiplicative functions which we shall find is very fruitful.

Theorem 2.10a.   If $f(n)$ is a multiplicative function and

$$F(n) = \sum_{d|n} f(d),$$

then $F(n)$ is a multiplicative function.

First of all, the notation should be explained. The quantity on the right is the summation of $f(d)$ over all divisors d of n. For instance,

$$F(6) = f(1) + f(2) + f(3) + f(6), \ F(2) = f(1) + f(2), \ F(3) = f(1) + f(3).$$

Then $F(2)F(3) = f(1)f(1) + f(1)f(2) + f(1)f(3) + f(2)f(3)$, which is equal to $F(6)$ if f is multiplicative.   To prove the theorem we assume $(b,c) = 1$ and have

$$F(bc) = \sum_{d|bc} f(d) = \sum_{\substack{r|b \\ s|c}} f(rs) = \sum_{\substack{r|b \\ s|c}} f(r)f(s) =$$
$$\sum_{r|b} f(r) \sum_{s|c} f(s) = F(b) \cdot F(c).$$

The first equality is by definition; the second holds since any divisor of bc must be the product of a divisor of b, and a divisor of c, since $(b,c) = 1$. The third equality results from the multiplicative character of the function f.   This completes the proof.

Now $\sum_{d|p^n} \phi(d) = 1 + \phi(p) + \phi(p^2) + \cdots + \phi(p^n)$, since the only divisors of p^n are powers of p, p being a prime.   This shows that

$$\sum_{d|p^n} \phi(d) = 1 + p - 1 + p^2 - p + p^3 - p^2 + \cdots + p^n - p^{n-1} = p^n,$$

which is a particular case of the following theorem.

Theorem 2.10b. $\sum_{d|n} \phi(d) = n$.

From Theorem 2.10a we know that $\sum_{d|n} \phi(d)$ is a multiplicative function, since the Euler Phi-function is multiplicative.   Hence

$$\sum_{d|n} \phi(d) = \sum_{d|p_1^{a_1}} \phi(d) \cdot \sum_{d|p_2^{a_2}} \phi(d) \cdot \cdots \sum_{d|p_r^{a_r}} \phi(d),$$

where $n = p_1^{a_1} p_2^{a_2} \cdots p_r^{a_r}$. However, each sum is equal to the power of p contained therein, which proves our theorem.

2.11. Wilson's Theorem and an allied result

There is an interesting theorem called Wilson's Theorem (Ref. 11, pp. 259 ff.), which a trick helps us to prove easily.

Theorem 2.11a. If p is a prime, $(p-1)! \equiv -1 \pmod{p}$.

First notice that the converse of this theorem is easy to prove; namely, $(m-1)! \equiv -1 \pmod{m}$ implies that m is a prime, for otherwise $(m-1)!$ has a factor in common with m. Hence the theorem gives a necessary and sufficient condition that m be a prime.   See Exercise 12, below.

To prove the theorem, write out the set of numbers

$$1, 2, 3, \cdots, p - 2, p - 1,$$

and let the "mate" of 2 be that number a_2 of the set for which $2a_2 \equiv 1$ (mod p). (We know there is such a number, since 2 is prime to p.) Conversely, the mate of a_2 is 2. Then we can associate 3 with its mate, and so on. If a number b were its own mate, we would have $b^2 \equiv 1$ (mod p); that is, $(b - 1)(b + 1) \equiv 0$ (mod p), which implies that $b = 1$ or $p - 1$. Hence omitting these two numbers, we have

$$(p - 2)! \equiv (2a_2)(\cdot\cdot)(\cdot\cdot) \cdots (\cdot\cdot) \ (\text{mod } p),$$

where each parenthesis contains two numbers whose product is congruent to 1 (mod p). Hence we have

$$(p - 1)! \equiv 1(1)(1) \cdots (1)(p - 1) \equiv -1 \ (\text{mod } p).$$

This is perhaps clarified by an example. Take $p = 11$. Then $2x \equiv 1$ (mod 11) has the solution 6, and hence 2 and 6 are mates. The mate of 3 is 4, and so on. Then we can write

$$10! \equiv 1(2 \cdot 6)(3 \cdot 4)(5 \cdot 9)(7 \cdot 8)(10) \equiv 1 \cdot 1 \cdot 1 \cdot 1 \cdot 1 \cdot (-1) \ (\text{mod } 11).$$

A similar trick results in a proof of

Theorem 2.11b. If $r = (p - 1)/2$, then $(r!)^2(-1)^r \equiv -1$ (mod p) if p is a prime.

This is proved by pairing the numbers $1, 2, \cdots, p - 1$ as follows: 1 and -1, whose product is -1; 2 and $p - 2$, whose product is congruent to -2^2; 3 and $p - 3$, whose product is congruent to $-3^2, \cdots; (p - 1)/2$ and $(p + 1)/2$, whose product is congruent to $-r^2$, since $(p + 1)/2 = p - (p - 1)/2$. Hence $(p - 1)! \equiv (-1)(-2^2)(-3^2) \cdots (-r^2)$ (mod p). However, there are r minus signs, which shows that $(p - 1)! \equiv (-1)^r(r!)^2$ (mod p).

2.12. Perfect numbers

There is an interesting result connected with the σ function, where $\sigma(n)$ is the sum of the positive divisors of n. The number 6 has the property that it is the sum of its divisors not including 6; that is, $6 = 1 + 2 + 3$. (The positive divisors of a number less than the number are called its

aliquot parts or proper divisors.) Similarly, $28 = 1 + 2 + 4 + 7 + 14$. Any number which is the sum of its aliquot parts, that is, half the sum of all its positive divisors, is called a **perfect number.** It has been shown (Ref. 13) that no odd perfect number contains less than five different prime factors, but no odd perfect number has ever been found. On the other hand, Euclid developed a formula for all even perfect numbers. This may be found as follows: Let n be a perfect number written in the form $n = 2^{q-1}m$, where m is odd and q is greater than 1. Then $\sigma(n) = 2n$ implies

$$\sigma(2^{q-1})\sigma(m) = 2^q m;$$

that is,

$$(2^q - 1)\sigma(m) = 2^q m.$$

Since 2^q does not divide $2^q - 1$, it must divide $\sigma(m)$, and we may write $\sigma(m) = 2^q s$, which yields

$$(2^q - 1)s = m.$$

Certainly m has two divisors: s and $(2^q - 1)s$, whose sum is $2^q s$ or m, whereas we have just learned that $\sigma(m) = 2^q s$. Hence s and $2^q - 1$ are the only divisors of m, a fact which shows that $s = 1$ and $2^q - 1$ is a prime p. In that case, n is a perfect number. Hence the even perfect numbers are those which can be written in the form

(1) $\qquad\qquad 2^{q-1}(2^q - 1)$ with $2^q - 1$, a prime number.

In fact, q must itself be a prime number, since if $q = ab$, $2^q - 1$ would have $2^a - 1$ as a factor.

However, q may be a prime number without $2^q - 1$ being a prime number. For example, $2^{11} - 1$ is composite (see Exercise 5 in Section 2.9). The numbers $2^q - 1$ with q a prime are called **Mersenne numbers,** since it was Mersenne who conjectured that for $q \leqq 257$ only the following values of q yield prime values for $2^q - 1$:

$$2, 3, 5, 7, 13, 17, 19, 31, 67, 127, 257.$$

The fact that Mersenne made five errors, namely, $q = 67,257$ yield composite numbers, and $q = 61,89,107$ yield primes, has been shown (Bulletin of the American Mathematical Society [1948], Vol. 49, pp. 378–380). Recently five more Mersenne numbers have been found with the aid of high-speed calculating machines, namely, for $q = 521,607,1279,2203,2281$.

(See two articles by Horace S. Uhler, Vol. 18 [1952] and Vol. 19 [1953] of *Scripta Mathematica*.)

The term "perfect number" had its origin in the mystical meanings of numbers. Amicable numbers are similarly defined. (Ref. 11, pp. 96–100 and Ref. 14, p. 83.)

2.13. Fermat numbers

It is known that regular polygons with $2,4,8,16, \cdots$ sides may be constructed with ruler and compasses when the former is used only to draw straight lines and the latter only to draw arcs. The regular pentagon may also be constructed with ruler and compasses. In fact, it can be proved (Ref. 16) that the regular polygons which can be so constructed are those of n sides, where

$$n = 2^k p_1 p_2 \cdots p_r,$$

with k a nonnegative integer and with the p's distinct primes such that $p - 1$ is a power of 2. Thus the polygons of less than 20 sides which can be constructed with ruler and compasses are those having

$$3, 4, 5, 6, 8, 10, 12, 15, 16, 17$$

sides. If $p = 2^r + 1$ is a prime, it may be shown (why?) that r is a power of 2 and the numbers

$$2^{2^n} + 1$$

for n a nonnegative integer are called **Fermat numbers.** Fermat conjectured that all such numbers are primes. For $n = 0,1,2,3,4$ we have the respective primes

$$3 , 5 , 17 , 257 , 65537.$$

However, Fermat's conjecture is false. In fact, no other values of n are known which yield primes. It has been shown that Fermat numbers are composite for the following values of n:

$$5 , 6 , 7 , 8 , 9 , 11 , 12 , 18 , 23 , 36 , 38 , 73.$$

(Ref. 6, pp. 14, 15.) For example, $2^{2^5} + 1 = 641 \cdot 6700417$.

Exercises 2.13

1. If $2^r + 1$ is a prime, show that r is a power of 2.

2. If r is defined as in Theorem 2.11b, prove that $(r!)^2 \equiv -1 \pmod{p}$ if $p \equiv 1 \pmod 4$ and that $(r!)^2 \equiv 1 \pmod{p}$ if $p \equiv -1 \pmod 4$. The former congruence proves that $x^2 \equiv -1 \pmod{p}$ is solvable if $p \equiv 1 \pmod 4$.

3. Prove that if p is a prime, $r = (p-1)/2$ and $r! \equiv -1 \pmod p$, then $p \equiv -1 \pmod 4$. Is the converse of this statement true?

4. Suppose in the proof of Theorem 2.11a, the numbers $1, 2, \cdots, p - 1$ were paired so that the product of each pair is congruent to -1. Show that if $x^2 \equiv -1 \pmod p$ has no solution, then

$$(p - 1)! \equiv (-1)^r \pmod p;$$

that if $x^2 \equiv -1 \pmod p$ has a solution, then

$$(p - 1)! \equiv (-1)^{r-1} \pmod p;$$

and hence in the respective cases, r is even or odd.

5. Use the results of Exercise 4 to show that if $x^2 \equiv -1 \pmod p$ is solvable then $p \equiv 1 \pmod 4$.

6. Compute the first four even perfect numbers.

7. The first four even perfect numbers end alternately in 6 and 8. Does this property hold in general? If not, is it at least true that every even perfect number ends in either 6 or 8?

8. Since an equilateral triangle and a regular pentagon may be constructed with ruler and compasses, we can divide the circumference of a circle into 3 equal parts and 5 equal parts by such construction. Show how this may be used to divide the circumference into 15 equal parts without using the result on page 58. Generalize this result to show that if regular polygons of a and b sides, respectively, may be constructed, where $(a,b) = 1$, then a regular polygon of ab sides may be constructed.

9. Prove that $\sigma(n)$, the sum of the divisors of n, is a multiplicative function. Find $\sigma(p^n)$ and use these results to get formulas for $\sigma(n)$ and $\sum_{d|n} \sigma(d)$.

10. Prove that $d(n)$, the number of divisors of n, is a multiplicative function. Find $d(p^n)$ and use these results to get formulas for $d(n)$ and $\sum_{n|x} d(n)$, where x is a given integer.

11. Is the product of the divisors of n a multiplicative function?

12. Show that if $(m - 1)! \equiv -1 \pmod{m}$ then m is a prime number. For what numbers m is $(m - 1)! \equiv 0 \pmod{m}$?

2.14. The Chinese Remainder Theorem

There is an old puzzle attributed to Sun-Tsu in the first century A.D. which may be written as follows: Find the least two positive integers having the remainders 2,3,2 when divided by 3, 5, and 7, respectively. Let us see how this puzzle may be solved. All numbers having the remainder 2 when divided by 3 will be of the form $3n + 2$ for some integer n. If $3n + 2 \equiv 3 \pmod{5}$, it will have the remainder 3 when divided by 5. Then $3n \equiv 1 \pmod{5}$, which implies that $n \equiv 2 \pmod{5}$ or $n = 2 + 5x$; that is, $3n + 2 = 8 + 15x$. This gives all numbers which have the required remainders $\pmod{3}$ and $\pmod{5}$. We want $8 + 15x$ to be congruent to 2 $\pmod{7}$; that is, $8 + 15x \equiv 2 \pmod{7}$, or $x \equiv 1 \pmod{7}$. This gives $x = 1 + 7y$ and $3n + 2 = 23 + 105y$. Thus the two smallest positive numbers satisfying the conditions are 23 and 128. Notice that we began with a solution for 3 and got one for 5, thus one for 15; our last step gave a solution mod $3 \cdot 5 \cdot 7$. That this process always works if the successive moduli are relatively prime is shown by

Theorem 2.14. If $(b,c) = 1$ and r and s are any two numbers, there is a number $x \equiv r \pmod{b}$ and $\equiv s \pmod{c}$.

To prove this, notice that $x \equiv r \pmod{b}$ if and only if x is of the form $r + bt$ for an integer t. Then we may determine t so that $r + bt \equiv s \pmod{c}$, since b and c are relatively prime.

Notice that if x and y are two integers which satisfy the conditions of Theorem 2.14, their difference is divisible by b and by c and hence by bc. Furthermore, if x is a solution, $x - tbc$ is a solution for any t. This yields the

Corollary 2.14a. There is just one nonnegative integer x less than bc satisfying the congruences of the theorem, and all solutions are congruent to $x \pmod{bc}$.

Corollary 2.14b. If $m_1, m_2, \cdots, m_r$ are relatively prime in pairs and $a_1, a_2, \cdots, a_r$ are any r integers, the congruences below have a common solution:

$$x \equiv a_1 \pmod{m_1}, \; x \equiv a_2 \pmod{m_2}, \cdots, x \equiv a_r \pmod{m_r}.$$

Corollary 2.14b often goes by the name of the Chinese Remainder Theorem, since such problems have been found in ancient Chinese literature. In fact much mathematical development in China in connection with the theory of numbers antedated by centuries corresponding mathematics in Europe. (Ref. 4, Vol. 2, p. 57.)

Exercises 2.14

1. A woman with a basket of eggs was knocked down by a bicycle. In presenting her bill to the rider's father, she said she did not know how many eggs she had but when she counted them two at a time there was one egg left, and similarly when she counted them three, four, five, and six at a time; but in sevens there were not any left over. What is the smallest number of eggs she could have had?

2. If any or all of the following sets of congruences have a solution, find the solution:

   a. $x \equiv 3 \pmod 6$, $x \equiv 1 \pmod 7$, $x \equiv 2 \pmod{18}$.
   b. $x \equiv 2 \pmod{10}$, $x \equiv 7 \pmod{15}$, $x \equiv -4 \pmod 6$.
   c. $x \equiv 3 \pmod 4$, $x \equiv 5 \pmod 7$, $x \equiv 7 \pmod 9$.

3. Describe a method of finding solutions of a set of congruences in which the moduli are not relatively prime.

Diophantine Equations

3.1. Introduction

A typical puzzle problem is the following: A man bought a number of cows at \$70 apiece and pigs at \$50 apiece. He spent, in all, \$530. How much of each did he buy? If c is the number of cows and p the number of pigs, we have the equation

$$70c + 50p = 530,$$

which is equivalent to the equation

$$7c + 5p = 53.$$

Now, if we could have fractional values of the unknowns, we could assign any value to p and solve for c. However, the values of p and c must be integers. Any equation whose solutions are restricted to integers is called a **Diophantine Equation,** after Diophantos (Ref. 11, p. 179). In this case, there is a further restriction that the solutions must not only be integers but cannot be negative. It can be solved by trial if we notice that we need to find a c such that $53 - 7c$ is divisible by 5. If we try in order $c = 1,2,3,4$ we find that the last is the first acceptable value, the values $c = 5,6,7$ are not acceptable and any larger value of c would make p negative. Thus the only solution which fits the problem is $c = 4$, $p = 5$.

There is a better way to solve the problem. Notice that to make $53 - 7c$ divisible by 5 is to solve the congruence $53 \equiv 7c \pmod 5$. This is equivalent to solving $3 \equiv 2c \pmod 5$; that is, $8 \equiv 2c \pmod 5$, which has the solution $c \equiv 4 \pmod 5$. Hence all values of c must be of the form $4 + 5n$. Now n must be nonnegative if c is, and it cannot be as great as

1 if p is positive. In fact, if we replace c by $4 + 5n$ in the equation we have $28 + 35n + 5p = 53$, or $35n + 5p = 25$; that is, $7n + p = 5$. So our general solution is $c = 4 + 5n$, $p = 5 - 7n$ for integer values of n. This shows that $n = 0$ if c and p are positive. It is also possible to begin by solving the congruence $53 \equiv 5p \pmod{7}$, but this is longer.

Exercises 3.1

1. Solve the following Diophantine Equations, indicating all solutions in integers:

   a. $5x + 11y = 92$.
   b. $10x + 14y = 39$.
   c. $20x + 17y = 93$.

2. A man received a check for a certain amount of money, but on cashing it the cashier mistook the number of dollars for the number of cents and conversely. Not noticing this, the man then spent 68 cents and discovered to his amazement that he had twice as much money as the check was originally drawn for. Determine the amount of money for which the check must have been written.

3. Under what conditions on a, b, and c will $ax + by = c$ have one or more solutions in integers? Supposing that x_0 and y_0 is one pair of solutions, what formulas will include all solutions?

3.2. A method of solution of a linear Diophantine Equation in two unknowns

An equation $ax + by = c$ is called linear, since it contains no terms of higher degree than 1 in x and y. Solving this equation is equivalent to solving the congruence $ax \equiv c \pmod{b}$. This is solvable if and only if the g.c.d. of a and b divides c, from Theorem 2.5a. If the g.c.d. of a and b divides c, we can divide all three letters by the g.c.d. and have an equation in which a and b are relatively prime. Then if x_0 is one solution of the congruence $ax \equiv c \pmod{b}$ with $(a,b) = 1$, all solutions are of the form $x_0 + bn$, since $ax \equiv ay \pmod{b}$ implies $x \equiv y \pmod{b}$. Putting this in the equation gives $a(x_0 + bn) + by = c$; that is, $by = c - ax_0 - abn$

However, $ax_0 + by_0 = c$ implies that $c - ax_0 = by_0$, and $by = by_0 - abn$ implies $y = y_0 - an$. Thus we have

Theorem 3.2. The Diophantine Equation $ax + by = c$ has one or more solutions if and only if the g.c.d. of a and b divides c. If a and b are relatively prime and x_0, y_0 is one solution, all solutions are given by

$$x = x_0 + bn, \; y = y_0 - an$$

for integer values of n.

In this connection, geometrical considerations are of interest and value. The equation $ax + by = c$ represents a line in analytic geometry. The solutions in integers x and y will correspond to the points whose co-ordinates are integers and through which the line passes. We call any point whose coordinates are integers a **lattice point**. Thus, from the discussion above, there are no lattice points on the line $3x + 6y = 1$ and, from the previous section, only one lattice point in the first quadrant on the line $7x + 5y = 53$.

There are a number of ways of solving a linear congruence. We shall see in the next chapter that it may be done by means of continued fractions. Probably the best method in a numerical case for the solution of $ax \equiv b \pmod{m}$ aims at each stage to find a number congruent to b $\pmod{m}$ which has a factor in common with a and hence which can be divided into both sides of the congruence. Thus we can reduce the given congruence to one with smaller modulus and apply the method again and again to congruences with smaller and smaller moduli. We illustrate the method by solving

$$19x \equiv 73 \pmod{125}.$$

1. We seek a multiple of 125 which, when added to 73, gives a number divisible by 19. That is, we need a y such that $73 + 125y \equiv 0 \pmod{19}$. Since 73 is congruent to -3, and 125 to -8 (taking the smallest residues in absolute value), the last congruence becomes $-3 - 8y \equiv 0$ $\pmod{19}$, or $8y \equiv -3 \pmod{19}$.

2. We may see by inspection or use the same method to find $-3 \equiv 16$ $\pmod{19}$; that is, $8y \equiv 16 \pmod{19}$, which yields the solution $y = 2$.

This is the end of our "chain" of congruences, and, substituting $y = 2$ into $73 + 125y$, we get 323, which is $19 \cdot 17$. This shows that 17 is a solution of the given congruence.

This method may be used to prove the existence of solutions (see Exercise 14, below). It should be noticed that a Diophantine Equation $7x + 11y = 32$ can be reduced to a congruence (mod 11) or (mod 7) as shown above.

Exercises 3.2

1. Solve the two congruences, $69x \equiv 21 \pmod{96}$, $145x \equiv 35 \pmod{625}$.

2. What is the least positive value of c for which the line $15x + 21y = c$ has lattice points? What is the corresponding general result for the equation $ax + by = c$?

3. Find all positive solutions of the Diophantine Equation $23x + 37y = 212$.

4. How far apart are the lattice points on the line $7x + 5y = 53$? $7x + 5y = 1$? If a and b are relatively prime, how far apart will be the lattice points on the line $ax + by = c$?

5. Use the results of Exercise 4 to show that if a,b, and c are positive, $(a,b) = 1$ and $ab < c$, then the line $ax + by = c$ has at least one lattice point in the first quadrant not on either axis. What does this imply about the positive solutions?

6. If $(a,b) = 1$, show that the line $ax + by = c$ has infinitely many lattice points in the first quadrant if $ab < 0$, finitely many or none if $ab > 0$ with $ac > 0$, and none if $ab > 0$ with $ac < 0$.

7. If $(a,b) = 1$, and a,b, and c are positive, show that there are $(a + 1)(b + 1)$ lattice points within and on the rectangle whose vertices are $(0,0)$, $(b,0)$, $(0,a)$, (b,a). Hence show that within but not on the triangle bounded by the axes and the line $ax + by = ab$ there are exactly $(a - 1)(b - 1)/2$ lattice points, thus that there are exactly $(a - 1)(b - 1)/2$ positive values of c less than ab for which $ax + by = c$ has positive solutions.

8. Find the least integer b for which the equation $5x + 7y = b$ has exactly six positive solutions.

9. A customer buys an article for 48 cents. He has a $1 bill and 3 pennies, while the shopkeeper has 6 dimes and 7 nickels. In how many ways can

the change be arranged? (Ref. 14, p. 65; see also Exercises 11 and 12 in the same set.)

10. A typical problem in elementary algebra is the following: Each of two trains ran 180 miles, one at a speed of 6 miles per hour faster than the other. If the faster train required one hour less time find the speed of each. Suppose 6 is replaced by a and 180 by ad, find the speed in terms of a and d. Show that for integral a and d, the speed is an integer if and only if $d = t^2 + t$ for some integer t.

11. Show that the number of nonnegative solutions of the equation

$$x + 2y + 3z = n$$

is the integer nearest to $(n + 3)^2/12$. (Ref. 14, p. 66.) Graphical methods may be used.

12. How may Euler's Theorem be used to show the existence of a solution of the congruence $ax \equiv b \pmod{m}$ when $(a,m) = 1$? Would you consider this a practical method of numerical solution?

13. Show that $ax + by + cz = d$ has integer solutions if the g.c.d. of a,b,c divides d.

14. How may the method used in the numerical example of this section be used to show the existence of a solution of $ax \equiv b \pmod{m}$ when $(a,m) = 1$?

15. Prove the first part of Theorem 3.2, using Theorem 1.8d.

3.3. Linear Diophantine Equations in more than two unknowns

One might guess, as a generalization of results for an equation in two unknowns, the truth of the following:

Theorem 3.3. The Diophantine Equation

$$a_1x_1 + a_2x_2 + \cdots + a_nx_n = d$$

is solvable if and only if the g.c.d. of the a_i's divides d.

We prove this for $n = 3$ and leave to the reader the proof by induction for any n. Suppose g is the g.c.d. of a_1 and a_2. Then, no matter what integer y is, we can, from Theorem 3.2, solve

$$a_1x_1 + a_2x_2 = gy.$$

Thus the solution for $n = 3$ is reduced to finding integers y and x_3 such that $gy + a_3x_3 = d$. This has a solution if and only if the g.c.d. of g and a_3 divides d. However, the g.c.d. of g and a_3 is the same as the g.c.d. of a_1, a_2, a_3, since any divisor of g and a_3 divides a_1 and a_2, while any common divisor of a_1, a_2 and a_3 divides both g and a_3. This establishes our theorem.

The method of the proof may be used to find a solution in a numerical case as may be illustrated as follows: To solve

$$6x + 10y + 15z = 37,$$

notice that $6x + 10y = 2t$ is solvable for any t and a solution of $2t + 15z = 37$ is $t = 11, z = 1$. Hence the general solution of the latter is $t = 11 - 15u$, $z = 1 + 2u$. Then $6x + 10y = 2t$ implies $3x + 5y = 11 - 15u$ or $3x + 5(y + 3u) = 11$, and the general solution is

$$x = 2 + 5v, y + 3u = 1 - 3v, z = 1 + 2u.$$

Though the above example showed a solution when each pair of co-efficients had a common factor greater than 1, the final solution was somewhat special, since the coefficient of y divided that of u in $3x + 5y = 11 - 5u$. In general it would be considerably longer.

There is another method of solution whose motivation is not quite so clear but which gives results very expeditiously. The fundamental idea is this: Suppose the g.c.d. of a,b,c is 1. Then if we can find a',b',c' and a'',b'',c'' so that the determinant

$$\begin{vmatrix} a & b & c \\ a' & b' & c' \\ a'' & b'' & c'' \end{vmatrix}$$

is 1, we shall set up the equations

$$ax + by + cz = x',$$
$$a'x + b'y + c'z = y',$$
$$a''x + b''y + c''z = z'.$$

Since the determinant of the coefficients is 1, these may be solved for integers x,y, and z in terms of x',y', and z'; setting $x' = d$ and considering y' and z' arbitrary parameters, we have a general solution. The chief difficulty, then, is to find the second and third rows of the determinant. This may be done as follows: Let $g = (a,b)$ and $as - br = g$. Then

$(a,b,c) = 1$ implies $(g,c) = 1$, and there are integers u and v such that $gu - cv = 1$. Set up the determinant

$$\begin{vmatrix} a & b & c \\ r & s & 0 \\ av/g & bv/g & u \end{vmatrix}.$$

Expanding by the last column, we have $c(rbv/g - sav/g) + u(as - rb) = cv(rb - sa)/g + u(as - rb) = -cv + gu = 1$.

Let us see how this goes for a numerical example. To solve

$$8x + 10y + 3z = 34,$$

notice that $g = (8,10) = 2$ and $s = -1, r = -1$ is a solution of $8s - 10r = 2$, while $u = 2, v = 1$ is a solution of $2u - 3v = 1$. Thus we have

$$\begin{aligned} 8x + 10y + 3z &= z', \\ -x - y &= y', \\ 4x + 5y + 2z &= z'. \end{aligned}$$

Solving for x, y, and z gives us the equations

$$\begin{aligned} x &= -2x' - 5y' + 3z', \\ y &= 2x' + 4y' - 3z', \\ z &= -x' + 2z', \end{aligned}$$

and, putting $x' = 34$, we have the general solution in terms of the parameters y' and z'.

Another type of puzzle problem leads to two linear equations in three unknowns: A farmer with \$100 goes to market to buy a hundred head of stock. Prices were as follows: calves, \$10 each; pigs, \$3 each; chickens, \$.50 each. He gets exactly one hundred head for his \$100. How many of each does he buy? If we let c be the number of calves, p the number of pigs and f the number of chickens, we have the two equations:

$$\begin{aligned} 10c + 3p + \tfrac{1}{2}f &= 100, \\ c + p + f &= 100. \end{aligned}$$

If we subtract the second from twice the first, we have the equation

$$19c + 5p = 100,$$

and $100 \equiv 19c \pmod 5$ implies $c = 5u$ and hence $p = 20 - 19u$. Substitution in the second given equation gives $f = 80 + 14u$. Since the value of c must be nonnegative, u must be nonnegative, and p nonnegative implies $u \leqq 1$. Hence the only permissible answers are

0, 20, 80 for $u = 0$, and 5, 1, 94 for $u = 1$.

If there is to be at least one of each kind of stock, the second is the only answer.

Exercises 3.3

1. Three chickens and one duck sold for as much as two geese; one chicken, two ducks, and three geese were sold together for 25 shillings. What was the price of each bird in an exact number of shillings?

2. Find necessary and sufficient conditions that the equations

$$ax + by + cz = d,$$
$$a'x + b'y + c'z = d'$$

be solvable in integers.

3. Along the lines of the second method of solution of a single linear equation in three unknowns, develop one for the solution of two linear equations in three unknowns.

4. Find all the integer solutions of $x^2 - y^2 = 15$.

5. Show that if (x_1, y_1, z_1) and (x_2, y_2, z_2) are solutions of $ax + by + cz = d$ then $(x_1 - x_2, y_1 - y_2, z_1 - z_2)$ is a solution of $ax + by + cz = 0$. Find all the solutions of the latter and use this to show that all solutions of the former equation can be written in the form

$$x = x_1 + r_1 u + s_1 v,$$
$$y = y_1 + r_2 u + s_2 v,$$
$$z = z_1 + r_3 u + s_3 v,$$

where u and v are arbitrary integers and (r_1, r_2, r_3) and (s_1, s_2, s_3) are solutions of $ax + by + cz = 0$.

3.4. Quadratic Diophantine Equations

Quadratic Diophantine Equations arise, for example, in such problems as the following: Find an integer b such that the following equation leads to a "factorable" quadratic in the sense of intermediate algebra, that is, to a quadratic equation whose roots are rational numbers:

$$\frac{1}{x-1} + \frac{b}{x-4} = 1.$$

On multiplication and collection of terms we have the equation

$$x^2 - x(6+b) + b + 8 = 0.$$

If this is to have rational solutions, its discriminant must be a perfect square; that is, for some integer s,

$$s^2 = b^2 + 8b + 4 = (b+4)^2 - 12.$$

Thus we need to solve for b the Diophantine Equation

$$12 = (b+4)^2 - s^2.$$

Hence one factor of 12 must be $b + 4 + s$ and the other $b + 4 - s$. In symbols,

$$r = b + 4 + s,$$
$$t = b + 4 - s,$$

where $rt = 12$. Thus $r + t = 2(b+4)$ and $r - t = 2s$. Because of the factor 2 in the right members, these equations may be solved for integers b and s if and only if r and t are both odd or both even (we say briefly, "r and t are of the same parity"). Since interchanging r and t does not change b, we may choose r to be less than t in absolute value and have the following possible pairs of values for r and t:

$$r = \pm 1, t = \pm 12; r = \pm 2, t = \pm 6; r = \pm 3, t = \pm 4.$$

However, r and t must have the same parity, and hence the only values to be considered are

$$r = 2, t = 6 \text{ and } r = -2, t = -6,$$

which yield

$$b = 0 \text{ and } b = -8.$$

Only the latter value yields a quadratic equation. The same method may be used to prove

Theorem 3.4. The Diophantine Equation $x^2 - u^2y^2 = d$ has the solution $2x = r + t$, $2uy = r - t$, where $rt = d$ and $r - t \equiv 0 \pmod{2u}$.

The proof is left to the reader, who can also see that the equation has no solutions if $d \equiv 2 \pmod 4$.

Theorem 3.4 shows that such an equation has only a finite number of solutions. It may therefore seem remarkable that the equation

$$x^2 - cy^2 = d$$

has either no solution or an infinite number if c is not a square. If $d = 1$ this is the so-called **Pell Equation,** which is discussed more fully in the next chapter. At this point we shall be content to show that if x_0, y_0 is a solution of

$$x^2 - cy^2 = 1,$$

with y_0 not zero and c not a perfect square, there is an infinite number of solutions. To this end, let n be any positive integer and see that the expansion of $(x_0 - \sqrt{c}y_0)^n$ determines integers x and y by means of the following equation:

$$(x_0 - \sqrt{c}y_0)^n = x - \sqrt{c}y.$$

That is, x is the sum of all terms in the expansion of the left side of the equation in which the exponent of $\sqrt{c}$ is even, and $\sqrt{c}y$ all those for which the exponent of $\sqrt{c}$ is odd. If in each term of x we replace $-\sqrt{c}$ by $\sqrt{c}$, we produce no change; if we make the same replacement in the other terms, the sum becomes $+\sqrt{c} \cdot y$. Hence

$$(x_0 + \sqrt{c}y_0)^n = x + \sqrt{c}y.$$

Taking the product of the left sides of these two equations and setting it equal to the product of the right sides, we have

$$(x_0^2 - cy_0^2)^n = x^2 - cy^2.$$

The quantity in parentheses on the left side is 1, and hence the right side is 1 also and x, y is a solution of the Pell Equation. Since $(x_0 + \sqrt{c}y_0)^n$ increases with n, no pair of values of x and y for any n can be the same as any pair for another n.

In contrast to the above result for the Pell Equation there is a remarkable theorem of A. Thue, which is as follows: If

$$f(z) = a_n z^n + a_{n-1} z^{n-1} + \cdots + a_1 z + a_0, \ n \geq 3,$$

has integer coefficients and is irreducible, that is, has no polynomial factors with integer coefficients, then the equation

$$a_n x^n + a_{n-1} x^{n-1} y + \cdots + a_1 x y^{n-1} + a_0 y^n = c$$

has only a finite number of solutions in integers x and y, zero being finite. (Ref. 10, p. 260 ff.)

Exercises 3.4

1. For what integers b does

$$\frac{1}{x-1} + \frac{b}{x-3} = 1$$

yield a quadratic equation with rational roots?

2. Prove Theorem 3.4.

3. Show that if $x^2 - cy^2 = 1$ has a solution with $y \neq 0$ and $x^2 - cy^2 = d$ has a solution, then the latter equation has an infinite number of solutions if c is not a square.

3.5. Pythagorean numbers

There is a particular kind of quadratic Diophantine Equation which is connected with the right triangle. It is well known that there is a right triangle with sides 3,4, and 5.   This collection of numbers is called a **Pythagorean set**. To find all right triangles whose sides are integers we must solve the equation

$$x^2 + y^2 = z^2.$$

First, notice that if x,y,z is a solution, then bx,by,bz is also a solution; and, conversely, if any two of x,y, and z have a prime factor in common, it must divide the third, and, after division, we get another solution. Hence we may assume that no two have a factor in common. Such solutions we call **primitive solutions**; all solutions will then be multiples of these. Furthermore, if x and y were both odd, z^2 would be congruent to 2 (mod 4), which is impossible. They cannot both be even, since we have ruled out the case when they have a factor in common. Then suppose we let y be even and equal to $2u$. Thus we have reduced our problem to finding solutions of

$$x^2 + 4u^2 = z^2,$$

with x odd and no two of x,u,z having a factor in common.

The equation may then be written in the form

$$z^2 - x^2 = 4u^2;$$

that is,

$$z - x = 2r, z + x = 2s, rs = u^2,$$

since x and z are of like parity, which implies $z = r + s$, $x = s - r$. Now, if r and s had a prime factor in common, it would divide z and x. However, z and x are relatively prime, which implies that r and s are also. Thus $rs = u^2$ implies that r and s are squares which may be written $r = m^2$, $s = n^2$, with $mn = u$. This gives us

$$z = m^2 + n^2, x = n^2 - m^2, y = 2mn$$

as the complete solution of $x^2 + y^2 = z^2$. That is, for each pair of values of m and n we have a solution, and if x,y,z is a solution in which no two have a factor in common, there are integers m and n satisfying the above equations.

It is not hard to show that the Diophantine Equation $x^3 + y^3 = z^3$ has no solutions in positive integers x,y,z (Ref. 14, pp. 408 ff.). In fact, it is conjectured that

$$x^n + y^n = z^n$$

has no solution in positive integers if n is greater than 2. This conjecture is called Fermat's Last Theorem, and, in spite of the efforts of many mathematicians, has never been proved for all integers n.

3.6. Other Diophantine Equations

While there are systematic methods for solving many Diophantine Equations, many solutions depend on the ingenuity and observation of the solver. To show how such solutions may be effected, we consider the following problem:

For the fraction 16/64 one might erroneously cancel the 6's and arrive at 1/4, a correct result. If $\overline{ab}$ stands for the two-digit number $10a + b$, and $\overline{bc}$ for $10b + c$, for what fractions $\overline{ab}/\overline{bc}$ is the quotient equal to a/c where the numerator is a two-digit number with digits a and b, the denominator is a two-digit number with the digits b and c, and $b > 0$?

To solve this problem we need to find positive integers less than 10 such that

$$\frac{10a + b}{10b + c} = \frac{a}{c};$$

that is, $10ac + bc = 10ab + ca$, or

(1) $$10a(c - b) = c(a - b).$$

Now, 10 is a divisor of the right side, and it is not a divisor of either c nor $a - b$, since a, b, c are positive integers less than 10. Hence either c is even and $a - b$ is divisible by 5, or $a - b$ is even and c is divisible by 5. We consider these two cases separately.

1. $a - b \equiv 0 \pmod 5$ and $c = 2c'$ for an integer c'. Then $a - b = 0$ or ± 5. In the first case (1) shows that $c = b$, and our fraction is $\overline{aa}/\overline{aa}$. In the second (1) reduces to

$$(b \pm 5)(2c' - b) = \pm c'.$$

The left side is even, since the first or second factor is even according as b is odd or even. Since c' must then be not greater than 4 and since with the plus sign the left side would be greater than 4, the ambiguous sign must be negative. Then $a = b - 5 > 0$, and we have

$$(b - 5)(2c' - b) = -c', b > 5,$$

which becomes $b^2 - b(5 + 2c') + 9c' = 0$. Thus, if $c' = 2$, $b = 6$, $a = 1$; if $c' = 4$, $b = 9$, $a = 4$, and we have the fractions

$$16/64, 49/98.$$

2. $a - b = 2u, c = 5$. Then equation (1) gives

$$2a(5 - b) = a - b.$$

Since a divides the left side, it must divide the right side, and hence it is a divisor of b. Write $b = ka$, and substitute in the last equation to get

$$9 = k(2a - 1),$$

which shows that k divides 9 and hence is 1, 3 or 9. In the respective cases we get the fractions

$$55/55, \ 26/65, \ 19/95.$$

Thus the only solutions of our problem are

$$\overline{aa}/\overline{aa}, \ 16/64, \ 26/65, \ 19/95, \ 49/98.$$

Exercises 3.6

1. A mistake often made by beginners is to write

$$a/b + c/d = (a + c)/(b + d).$$

Assume b and d are positive integers and prime respectively to a and c. Find all solutions in integers of this equation.

2. The number 3025 has the property that if the numbers 30 and 25, formed from the digits in order of the two halves of the number, are added (giving 55) and the result squared (55^2) the result is the original number. How many other numbers are there composed of four different digits having the same property?

3. Show that if $a/b < c/d$ with b and d positive integers then

$$\frac{a}{b} < \frac{a+c}{b+d} < \frac{c}{d}.$$

Will the same result hold if we remove the restriction that the letters are integers?

Continued Fractions

4.1. The Fibonacci Sequence

There is a very interesting sequence of integers which bears the name of Fibonacci, an Italian mathematician of the twelfth century. The first few numbers of this sequence are

$$1, 1, 2, 3, 5, 8, 13, 21, 34, \cdots .$$

Each number is the sum of the two preceding ones. These numbers occur in nature in the following manner. If a twig or branch is selected, and, starting with one bud, one's hand moves to the nearest bud and so continues in spiral fashion around the twig until it reaches a bud just above the starting one, the number of intervening buds will be one of the Fibonacci numbers, and the number of revolutions around the stalk will be another such number, which ones depending on the particular plant. A pine cone gives a similar result.

We are concerned here, however, with the mathematical properties of the sequence. Notice that $1 \cdot 3 - 2^2 = -1, 2 \cdot 5 - 3^2 = 1, 3 \cdot 8 - 5^2 = -1,$ $5 \cdot 13 - 8^2 = 1$, and so on. This property is connected with a geometrical deception which may be familiar to the student. A square 8 units by 8 may be cut up as shown in the figure below and the pieces fitted together as shown to give a rectangle 5 by 13. The area is thus increased by 1 square unit. Notice that the numbers appearing are those of four successive numbers of the Fibonacci Sequence.

The property noted above is equivalent to the sequence of equations

$$1/2 - 2/3 = -1/6, 2/3 - 3/5 = 1/15, 3/5 - 5/8 = -1/40, \text{ etc.}$$

This means that if the quotients of successive terms are formed, their differences are alternately negative and positive and each is less in absolute value than the preceding. In other words, if we call u_n the nth term of the Fibonacci Sequence where 1 and 1 are the first two terms, the

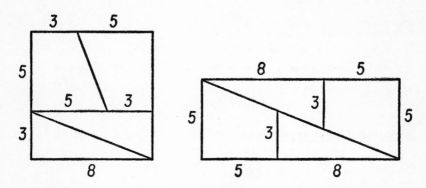

ratios u_n/u_{n+1} for $n > 0$ form a decreasing sequence for even values of n and an increasing sequence for odd values of n, each of the former ratios being greater than each of the latter. (This will be rigorously shown later.) The ratio u_n/u_{n+1} approaches a limiting value which we shall call k, associated with what the Greeks called the Golden Section. The rectangle the ratio of whose sides is $1/k$ was supposed to be the most beautiful.

There is an interesting trick by which one can give a closed expression for the nth term of the Fibonacci Sequence and many other sequences similarly determined. First of all, consider the Fibonacci Sequence and notice that the nth term is given in terms of the two preceding ones by means of the formula

(1) $$u_n = u_{n-1} + u_{n-2}.$$

The trick is to set

(2) $$u = c\alpha^n + d\beta^n$$

and show that c, d, α, and β may be determined so that $u_1 = 1$, $u_2 = 1$ and (1) holds. It will then follow that (2) gives a formula for the terms of the Fibonacci Sequence.

First, we find how α and β can be chosen so that (1) will be satisfied. If (1) is to hold, the following equation must be true:

$$c\alpha^n + d\beta^n = c\alpha^{n-1} + d\beta^{n-1} + c\alpha^{n-2} + d\beta^{n-2}.$$

The coefficients of c and d in this equation are

$$\alpha^{n-2}(\alpha^2 - \alpha - 1) \text{ and } \beta^{n-2}(\beta^2 - \beta - 1),$$

respectively. Hence the last equation will be satisfied if α and β are the roots of the equation

(3) $x^2 - x - 1 = 0.$

For this choice (1) will hold whatever the values of c and d.

Second, we choose c and d so that $u_1 = 1$ and $u_2 = 1$; that is,

$$1 = c\alpha + d\beta,$$
$$1 = c\alpha^2 + d\beta^2.$$

Since $\alpha \neq \beta$ these equations can be solved for c and d with the following result:

$$c = \frac{\beta - 1}{\alpha(\beta - \alpha)}, \, d = \frac{1 - \alpha}{\beta(\beta - \alpha)}.$$

Then, if we denote by α the root $(1 - \sqrt{5})/2$ of (3) and β the other root, we see that $\beta - \alpha$ is equal to $\sqrt{5}$, and a little manipulation shows that

$$c = -1/\sqrt{5}, d = 1/\sqrt{5}.$$

Hence

(4) $u_n = (\beta^n - \alpha^n)/\sqrt{5}.$

Exercises 4.1

1. Using the numbers 5,8,13,21, dissect the square 13 inches on a side in a fashion similar to that in the figure above.

2. Using the formula (1) for u_n of the Fibonacci Sequence given above, show that

$$u_n u_{n+2} - u_{n+1}^2 = (-1)^{n+1}.$$

HINT: Show that the left side is equal to $-(u_{n-1}u_{n+1} - u_n^2)$. Achieve the same result using formula (4).

3. Using previous results, find $\lim\limits_{n \to \infty} u_n$ for the Fibonacci Sequence.

4. Consider the sequence

$$1, 1, 3, 7, 17, \cdots,$$

in which $u_1 = 1$, $u_2 = 1$, and $u_n = 2u_{n-1} + u_{n-2}$. Using the methods used for the Fibonacci Sequence, find a formula for the nth term.

5. If the equation $x^2 - ax - b = 0$ has two distinct roots, α and β, where $\beta > \alpha$, and if the sequence of integers u_n is defined by its first two terms and the equation

$$u_n = au_{n-1} + bu_{n-2},$$

show that a formula for u_n is

$$u_n = (\beta u_1 - u_2)\alpha^{n-1}/q + (u_2 - \alpha u_1)\beta^{n-1}/q,$$

where $q = \sqrt{a^2 + 4b}$.

6. If in the sequence defined in the previous exercise $|\alpha| > |\beta|$ show that u_n/u_{n-1} approaches α as n becomes infinite. Is there a limit if $\alpha = -\beta$? If so, find it; if not, show why not.

7. If in Exercise 5, $\alpha = \beta$ show that the nth term of the sequence is given by the formula

$$u_n = c\alpha^n + nd\alpha^n,$$

where α is the root of $x^2 - ax - b = 0$, $c = 4(au_1 - u_2)/a^2$ and $d = 2(2u_2 - au_1)/a^2$. Note that $\alpha = a/2$. In this case will u_n/u_{n-1} approach a limit as n becomes infinite? If so, find it; if not, show why not.

8. Suppose we have two sequences whose nth terms are p_n and q_n, respectively, where $p_n = p_{n-1} + p_{n-2}$, $q_n = q_{n-1} + q_{n-2}$ and $p_1 = 1$, $p_2 = 2$, while $q_1 = 4$, $q_2 = 7$. Prove

$$p_n q_{n-1} - q_n p_{n-1} = (-1)^n.$$

4.2. Properties of Fibonacci-like Sequences

As we found from the exercises above, there are many sequences having many of the properties of the Fibonacci Sequence. In fact, we may combine the types mentioned in Exercises 5 and 6 above and consider the pair of sequences p_k, q_k, where

(1) $$p_k = a_k p_{k-1} + p_{k-2}, \quad q_k = a_k q_{k-1} + q_{k-2}.$$

Now

$$p_k q_{k-1} - q_k p_{k-1} = \begin{vmatrix} p_k & p_{k-1} \\ & \\ q_k & q_{k-1} \end{vmatrix} = \begin{vmatrix} a_k p_{k-1} + p_{k-2} & p_{k-1} \\ & \\ a_k q_{k-1} + q_{k-2} & q_{k-1} \end{vmatrix} = \begin{vmatrix} p_{k-2} & p_{k-1} \\ & \\ q_{k-2} & q_{k-1} \end{vmatrix}.$$

The second equality follows from (1), and the third is obtained by subtracting a_k times the second column from the first, an operation which we know leaves unaltered the value of the determinant. Thus, noticing that the last determinant is equal to

$$-(p_{k-1}q_{k-2} - q_{k-1}p_{k-2}),$$

we see that if in the expression $p_k q_{k-1} - q_k p_{k-1}$ we decrease the subscripts by 1 we merely change its sign. Hence, if we decrease the subscripts by $k - 2$, we change the sign $k - 2$ times; k diminished by $k - 2$ is 2, and we have

$$(2) \quad (p_k q_{k-1} - q_k p_{k-1}) = (-1)^{k-2}(p_2 q_1 - q_2 p_1) = (-1)^k(p_2 q_1 - q_2 p_1).$$

Thus we have proved

Theorem 4.2a. If p_k and q_k are the kth terms of two sequences defined by the equations (1) and if $p_2 q_1 - q_2 p_1 = 1$, then

$$p_k q_{k-1} - q_k p_{k-1} = (-1)^k.$$

An immediate consequence of the theorem is

$$(3) \quad\quad p_k/q_k - p_{k-1}/q_{k-1} = (-1)^k/(q_k q_{k-1});$$

that is, two consecutive quotients differ in absolute value by $1/q_k q_{k-1}$, and the differences alternate in sign. Furthermore,

$$p_k q_{k-2} - q_k p_{k-2} = \begin{vmatrix} p_k & p_{k-2} \\ q_k & q_{k-2} \end{vmatrix} = \begin{vmatrix} a_k p_{k-1} + p_{k-2} & p_{k-2} \\ a_k q_{k-1} + q_{k-2} & q_{k-2} \end{vmatrix}$$

$$= a_k \begin{vmatrix} p_{k-1} & p_{k-2} \\ q_{k-1} & q_{k-2} \end{vmatrix} = a_k(-1)^{k-1},$$

where the third equality results from subtracting the second column of the determinant from the first. Thus we have

Theorem 4.2b. If p_k and q_k satisfy the conditions of Theorem 4.2a and a_k is positive, then the fractions p_k/q_k form a decreasing sequence for k even and an increasing sequence for k odd.

Let us see now what we have just proved in terms of the Fibonacci

Sequence with which we started. In equations (1) let $a_k = 1$ for every k, and choose

$$p_1 = 1,\ p_0 = 0,\ q_1 = 1,\ q_0 = 1.$$

Then we will have the following table of values for p_k and q_k:

k	0	1	2	3	4	5	6	7	8	9	10	11
p_k	0	1	1	2	3	5	8	13	21	34	55	89
q_k	1	1	2	3	5	8	13	21	34	55	89	144 $\cdots$.

Thus the p_k and q_k range over the Fibonacci Sequence with $q_k = p_{k+1}$. Furthermore, if u_k is the kth term of the Fibonacci Sequence, we have

$$u_k = p_k = q_{k-1}.$$

Hence equation (3) becomes

$$u_k/u_{k+1} - u_{k-1}/u_k = (-1)^k/(u_{k+1}u_k).$$

Theorem 4.2a states (notice that for the choice above $p_2 q_1 - q_2 p_1 = 1$)

$$u_k^2 - u_{k-1}u_{k+1} = (-1)^k,$$

and Theorem 4.2b states that u_k/u_{k+1} form a decreasing sequence for k even and an increasing sequence for k odd. These are the results which we found empirically and have now established.

In an exercise it was shown that the ratios u_k/u_{k+1} approach a limit. We are now in a position to show that under the conditions of Theorem 4.2a the ratios p_k/q_k approach a limit. By "approaching a limit" we mean that there is some number L so that, by choosing k large enough, we can make

$$|L - p_k/q_k|$$

as small as we please. We have seen that the quotients p_k/q_k form a decreasing sequence for k even, and an increasing sequence for k odd. Furthermore, each even-numbered ratio is greater than every odd-numbered ratio, since if r is greater than k

$$p_{2k}/q_{2k} > p_{2r}/q_{2r} > p_{2r-1}/q_{2r-1}.$$

However, these properties alone do not guarantee the existence of a limit, as is shown by the following sequence:

$$-1, 4, 0, 3 + 1/2,\ 1 - 1/2,\ 3 + 1/4,\ 1 - 1/4,\ 3 + 1/8,\ 1 - 1/8,\ \cdots .$$

Here the even-numbered terms (second, fourth, and so on) form a decreasing sequence, the odd-numbered terms form an increasing sequence, and each of the former is greater than all of the latter. However, the terms of the sequence do not approach a limit since the even-numbered terms approach 3 and the odd-numbered terms approach 1. The difference between successive terms approaches $3 - 1$, which is 2. For the existence of a limit we must prove that the difference between successive terms approaches zero. This is easily done for the ratios p_k/q_k; for, from (3), the differences between successive quotients of the sequences (1) are in absolute value equal to the following:

$$\text{(4)} \qquad\qquad 1/(q_2 q_1),\ 1/(q_3 q_2),\ 1/(q_4 q_3),\ \cdots\ ,$$

where the products in the denominators form an increasing sequence of positive integers. Hence the fractions in (4) certainly decrease more rapidly than $1/2,\ 1/3,\ 1/4,\ \cdots$, which approach zero.

Suppose, then, we define a regular pair of sequences to be sequences p_k and q_k defined by the relationship (1) with a_k positive integers and $p_2 q_1 - q_2 p_1 = 1$. Then we may summarize the results so far obtained in

Theorem 4.2c. If p_k and q_k are the kth terms of a regular pair of sequences, they satisfy the conditions of Theorem 4.2a, and the quotient p_k/q_k approaches a limiting value as k increases without bound.

4.3.   Simple continued fractions

Regular pairs of sequences are connected with so-called continued fractions, which have many uses and interesting properties. A continued fraction is a number of the form

$$a_1 + \cfrac{b_2}{a_2 + \cfrac{b_3}{a_3 + \cfrac{b_4}{a_4 + \cdots}}},$$

where no a_i except perhaps the first is zero. If the b_i's are all 1 and the a_i's positive integers, except that the first may be zero, we call it a **simple continued fraction,** and it is only this kind of continued fraction that is to be considered here. From now on we use the term "continued fraction" instead of "simple continued fraction." Such fractions may be written much more compactly in the form

$$f = (a_1, a_2, \cdots),$$

since, knowing the a_i's, we can easily write the longer form. Such a fraction may or may not have a last term. In the latter case we call it an **infinite continued fraction.**

If f is the continued fraction $(a_1, a_2, \cdots)$, we call a_1 its first **convergent,** (a_1, a_2) its second convergent, $\cdots$, $(a_1, a_2, \cdots, a_k)$ its kth convergent. The kth convergent may be written in the form p_k/q_k, where p_k and q_k are relatively prime positive integers.

The simplest continued fraction in a certain sense would be that in which the a's are all equal to 1. Its successive convergents are

$$(1) \qquad\qquad 1, 2, 3/2, 5/3, 8/5, \cdots,$$

which are the reciprocals of the quotients of successive numbers of the Fibonacci Sequence. We know from the previous section (why?) that these quotients converge to a limit and that hence the value of the continued fraction approaches a limit. So we may let

$$x = 1 + \cfrac{1}{1 + \cfrac{1}{1 + \cdots}} \quad \cdot$$

Since this continued fraction has the same value if we start with the second term as if we started with the first, we have

$$x = 1 + 1/x,$$

or $x^2 - x - 1 = 0$. Use of the formula for the solution of a quadratic equation yields

$$x = \frac{1 + \sqrt{5}}{2} = 1.618034 \cdots,$$

where the positive sign is chosen, since x is positive, and

$$1/x = \frac{\sqrt{5} - 1}{2} = x - 1 = .618034 \cdots.$$

Exercises 4.3

1. Find the limit approached by the quotients of successive terms of the sequence of Exercise 4 in Section 4.1. What would be the limit for

$$u_n = au_{n-1} + u_{n-2}?$$

2. Find the limiting value of the periodic continued fraction

$$(1, 2, 1, 2, 1, 2, \cdots).$$

For this continued fraction express p_k and q_k in terms of p_{k-1}, p_{k-2} and q_{k-1}, q_{k-2}, respectively.

3. Prove that $p_k q_{k-3} - q_k p_{k-3} = (a_k a_{k-1} + 1)(p_{k-4} q_{k-3} - q_{k-4} p_{k-3})$, where p_k/q_k is the kth convergent of a continued fraction.

4. What is wrong with the following "proof" that $1 + 3 + 9 + \cdots = -1/2$? Let $x = 1 + 3 + 3^2 + \cdots = 1 + 3(1 + 3 + 3^2 + \cdots)$. Hence $x = 1 + 3x$, which gives $x = -1/2$. What is the essential difference that makes this proof invalid while the similar proof above is valid? Does this method of proof suffice to evaluate $1 + 1/2 + 1/4 + 1/8 \cdots$?

4.4. Computation of the convergents of a continued fraction

Much of the labor of computation of convergents of a continued fraction may be avoided by establishing formulas for p_k and q_k. Computation shows that for the simple continued fraction $(a_1, a_2, \cdots, a_k)$ the first three convergents are

$$a_1, (a_1 a_2 + 1)/a_2, [a_3(a_1 a_2 + 1) + a_1]/(a_3 a_2 + 1).$$

From this it may be seen that

$$p_3 = a_3 p_2 + p_1, \quad q_3 = a_3 q_2 + q_1,$$

which is exactly the relationship (1) in Section 4.2 for $k = 3$. That this holds for all k is the statement of

Theorem 4.4a. If p_k/q_k is the kth convergent of the continued fraction $(a_1, a_2, \cdots)$, where p_k and q_k are positive, relatively prime integers, then

$$p_k = a_k p_{k-1} + p_{k-2}, \quad q_k = a_k q_{k-1} + q_{k-2}.$$

We have already shown this for $k = 3$. Let us assume that it holds for $k = r$ and show that this implies that it holds for $k = r + 1$; this will then prove the theorem by induction. Now

$$p_r/q_r = (a_1, a_2, \cdots, a_r),$$

and thus p_{r+1}/q_{r+1} will be obtained from this by replacing a_r by $a_r + 1/a_{r+1}$. If we make this replacement in $p_r/q_r = (a_r p_{r-1} + p_{r-2})/(a_r q_{r-1} + q_{r-2})$ we get

$$\frac{p_r}{q_r} = \frac{a_{r+1}(a_r p_{r-1} + p_{r-2}) + p_{r-1}}{a_{r+1}(a_r q_{r-1} + q_{r-2}) + q_{r-1}} = \frac{a_{r+1}p_r + p_{r-1}}{a_{r+1}q_r + q_{r-1}}.$$

Since the numerator and denominator of the fraction on the right are positive integers, to establish our result we need only to show that $a_{r+1}p_r + p_{r-1}$ and $a_{r+1}q_r + q_{r-1}$ are relatively prime. However,

$$\begin{vmatrix} a_{r+1}p_r + p_{r-1} & p_r \\ a_{r+1}q_r + q_{r-1} & q_r \end{vmatrix} = p_{r-1}q_r - q_{r-1}p_r = \pm 1,$$

by Theorem 4.2a, and any common factor of the elements of the first column of the determinant would have to divide 1; this shows that p_{r+1} and q_{r+1} are relatively prime and completes the proof of the theorem.

Since these relationships are the same as (1) in Section 4.2 and $p_2 q_1 - q_2 p_1 = 1$, the sequences p_k, q_k are regular sequences and we can conclude from Theorems 4.2a and 4.2c the truth of

Theorem 4.4b. If p_k/q_k is the kth convergent of a continued fraction,

$$p_k q_{k-1} - q_k p_{k-1} = (-1)^k,$$

and the continued fraction converges. The conditions of Theorem 4.2b also hold.

There is a systematic way to compute the convergents of a given continued fraction. To do this, notice that $p_1 = a_1$, $p_2 = a_1 a_2 + 1$ would permit us with consistency to define $p_0 = 1$ and $p_{-1} = 0$. In a similar fashion, we would have $q_0 = 0$ and $q_{-1} = 1$. Then suppose, for example, $a_1 = 1, a_2 = 2, a_3 = 3, \cdots$, and we form the following table:

a_i		1	2	3	4	5	6	
p_i	0	1	1	3	10	43	225	1393
q_i	1	0	1	2	7	30	157	972 ,

where the number 3 in the second line is $2 \cdot 1 + 1$, 10 is $3 \cdot 3 + 1$, and so forth, the third line being similarly computed.

Exercises 4.4

1. Find the first five convergents of each of the following continued fractions, the second and third being periodic (see Section 4.7):

   a. $(1,3,5,7, \cdots)$.
   b. $(1,\underline{2},2,2, \cdots)$.
   c. $(1,\underline{1},2,1,2,1,2, \cdots)$.

2. Show that the continued fraction of Example b above converges to $\sqrt{2}$ and that of Example c to $\sqrt{3}$.

3. Find the continued-fraction expansion of $355/113$, and compute the first three convergents.

4. Find the continued-fraction expansion of $\sqrt{5}$, compute the first three convergents, and compare your values with $\sqrt{5} = 2.236068$.

5. If $p_k/q_k = (a_1,a_2, \cdots,a_k)$, show that a_k is the greatest integer less than p_k/p_{k-1} and hence, from the result for all k, that

$$p_k/p_{k-1} = (a_k,a_{k-1}, \cdots,a_2,a_1).$$

6. If $q_k = p_{k-1}$, what can you conclude about the continued-fraction expansion of p_k/q_k?

7. Using the notations of Exercise 5, prove that $p_{k-1} = q_k$ implies

$$q_k^2 + (-1)^k \equiv 0 \pmod{p_k}.$$

Conversely, prove that the congruence and $p_k > q_k$ imply $p_{k-1} = q_k$. Hence state a necessary and sufficient condition that a finite continued fraction read the same forward as backward.

4.5.   Continued-fraction expansions

We have so far been chiefly concerned in finding the numbers to which continued fractions converge. Actually, from a computational point of view, it is of more importance to seek continued-fraction expansions of given numbers. This is useful, since, as we have seen, the various convergents give approximations to the number. For instance, one of the convergents of π is $22/7$, the familiar approximation, and no fraction with denominator smaller than 7 is a better approximation.

It is apparent from the form of the continued-fraction expansion that if x is the continued fraction $(a_1, a_2, \cdots)$ then a_1 is the greatest integer in x; that is, the largest integer not greater than x. We shall now illustrate the method of expansion, by three examples.

EXAMPLE 1. Find the continued-fraction expansion of $573/227$. Now, $573/227 = 2 + 1/x_2$, where $x_2 = 227/119 = 1 + 1/x_3$, where $x_3 = 119/108 = 1 + 1/x_4$, where $x_4 = 108/11 = 9 + 1/x_5$, where $x_5 = 11/9 = 1 + 1/x_6$, where $x_6 = 9/2 = 4 + 1/2$. Using the sequence of a_i's obtained in this manner, we have

$$
\begin{array}{ccccccc}
2 & 1 & 1 & 9 & 1 & 4 & 2 \\
0 \quad 1 & 2 & 3 & 5 & 48 & 53 & 260 \quad 573 \\
1 \quad 0 & 1 & 1 & 2 & 19 & 21 & 103 \quad 227.
\end{array}
$$

Notice that we might also have chosen $a_7 = 1$, $a_8 = 1$ in place of $a_7 = 2$, in which case the next to the last convergent would have been $313/124$.

EXAMPLE 2. Expand $\sqrt{17}$. Now $\sqrt{17} = 4 + 1/x_1$, where $x_1 = 1/(\sqrt{17} - 4) = \sqrt{17} + 4 = 8 + 1/x_2$. Since $x_2 = x_1$, the expansion of $\sqrt{17}$ is $(4,8,8, \cdots)$. To six places the value of $\sqrt{17}$ is 4.123106. We list below the first four convergents, their decimal values to six places, and their discrepancies from the true value.

Convergent	4	33/8	268/65	2177/528
Decimal value	4	4.125000	4.123069	4.123106
Discrepancy	−.123106	+0.001894	−0.000037	+0.000000

Actually, since we know that the true value of the number lies between any two successive convergents, we can tell from the expansion that 4.1231 is accurate to four places and 4.123069 to six. Notice that the continued fraction is periodic. We shall prove later that this is true of the continued-fraction expansion of any real quadratic surd (real root of a quadratic equation with integer coefficients).

EXAMPLE 3. Find the expansion $\sqrt[3]{2}$. This could be done somewhat along the lines of the above example, but there is a simpler way — a method which can be applied to get a positive solution of any polynomial equation. We seek, then, the real root of $x^3 - 2 = 0$. Since the root is between 1 and 2, we have $x = 1 + 1/x_1$, where x_1 is greater than 1. One may find the equation in x_1 by substitution in the given equation, but it is simpler to diminish the roots by 1 and reverse the order of the coefficients. Since the process usually employed in the theory of equations may be unfamiliar to the reader, we illustrate the mechanical process referring him to any college algebra text for the reasoning involved.

$$
\begin{array}{r|rrrr}
1\;] & 1 & 0 & 0 & -2 \\
 & & 1 & 1 & 1 \\
\hline
 & 1 & 1 & 1 & -1 \\
 & & 1 & 2 & \\
\hline
 & 1 & 2 & 3 & \\
 & & 1 & & \\
\hline
 & 1 & 3 & &
\end{array}
$$

Thus, if $x = 1 + y$, y satisfies the equation $y^3 + 3y^2 + 3y - 1 = 0$. Then $y = 1/x_1$ implies

$$1 + 3x_1 + 3x_1^2 - x_1^3 = 0, \text{ or}$$
$$x_1^3 - 3x_1^2 - 3x_1 - 1 = 0.$$

Notice that the last equation is obtained by reversing the order of coefficients and changing the signs. Further computation yields

$$x_1 = 3 + 1/x_2, \text{ where } 10x_2^3 - 6x_2^2 - 6x_2 - 1 = 0,$$
$$x_2 = 1 + 1/x_3, \text{ where } 3x_3^3 - 12x_3^2 - 24x_3 - 10 = 0,$$
$$x_3 = 5 + 1/x_4, \text{ where } 1 < x_4 < 2.$$

The computation of convergents and accuracy of results is as follows:

a_k		1	3	1	5	1
p_k	0	1	1	4	5	29	34
q_k	1	0	1	3	4	23	27
p_k/q_k		1.000	1.3333	1.2500	1.2609	1.2592
Discrepancy		-1.2599	$+.0734$	$-.0099$	$+.0010$	$-.0007$.

Notice that the larger the a_i the greater the gain in accuracy from one convergent to the next.

With the above examples in mind it is not hard to prove

Theorem 4.5a. The continued-fraction expansion of any real positive number is unique except that every rational number has two expansions:

$$(a_1, a_2, \cdots, a_{n-1}, a_n), \quad (a_1, a_2, \cdots, a_{n-1}, a_n', 1),$$

where $a_n = a_n' + 1$ and the first $n - 1$ of the a's are the same.

To prove this, let x_i be defined as that part of the expansion beginning with a_i, and x_{i+1} that beginning with a_{i+1}. Then $x_i = a_i + 1/x_{i+1}$, where $x_{i+1} \geqq 1$. If $x_{i+1} > 1$, this shows that a_i is the greatest integer in x_i and hence is uniquely determined. However, if $x_{i+1} = 1$, the continued faction may terminate with $(a_i + 1)$ or with $a_i + 1/1$. A terminating continued fraction, of course, represents a rational number. See Example 1 of this section.

Notice in this example that $p_6/q_6 = 260/103$ and a solution of $573x - 227y = -1$ is $x = q_6$, $y = p_6$. The next to the last convergent of the alternative expansion, $313/124$, similarly gives a solution of $573x - 227y = 1$. Why is this so? The following is left to the reader to prove.

Theorem 4.5b. If a/b is a positive rational number in lowest terms and if a/b is expanded into a continued fraction with k terms, then q_{k-1}, p_{k-1} is a solution of $ax - by = (-1)^k$.

This theorem gives a means of solving Diophantine Equations, linear in two unknowns, but it is not as good computationally as methods given previously in this book.

Exercises 4.5

1. Prove Theorem 4.5b above.

2. Using continued fractions, find a solution in integers of $13x - 23y = 1$.

3. Find the first five convergents in the continued-fraction expansion of 3.14159 and of 3.14160. Since π lies between these two numbers, what does this show about the continued-fraction expansion of π?

4. Find the continued-fraction expansion of $\sqrt{a^2 + 1}$, $\sqrt{a^2 + 2}$ for positive integers a.

5. Approximate by continued fractions accurate to three decimal places the positive root of $x^3 - 7x^2 = 1 = 0$.

4.6. Closeness of approximation

The convergent $355/113$ in the expansion of π was used as an approximation for this constant by the Babylonians. No fraction with smaller denominator gives a better approximation. Similarly, $22/7$ is the best approximation for the size of its denominator. In fact,

Theorem 4.6a. If p/q is a convergent of the continued-fraction expansion for a real number x_0, there is no rational number a/b with $b \leqq q$ which is closer to x_0.

The proof of this theorem will follow immediately from the

Lemma: If $a/b < c/d < a'/b'$ and $ab' - a'b = -1$, then d is greater than b and b'. (All letters represent positive integers.)

First, let us see why the theorem will follow from the lemma. Suppose p_k/q_k is the kth convergent in the expansion of x_0 and a/b is closer to x_0 than is p_k/q_k. Then a/b is between the kth and $k - 1$st convergent, since it is then either between x_0 and p_k/q_k or between x_0 and p_{k-1}/q_{k-1}. However, p_k/q_k and p_{k-1}/q_{k-1} satisfy the conditions of the lemma, and hence b is greater than q_k.

To prove the lemma, see that its conditions imply that

$$0 < c/d - a/b < a'/b' - a/b,$$
$$0 < (cb - ad)/db < (a'b - ab')/b'b = 1/bb'.$$

Hence $b'(cb - ad) < d$. However, $cb - ad$ is a positive integer, and therefore $b' < d$. Similarly, it may be shown that $b < d$.

It should be noticed that, though we know from the above theorem that if p_k/q_k and p_{k-1}/q_{k-1} are two successive convergents of x_0, there is then no rational number closer to x than p_k/q_k whose denominator does not exceed q_k; yet there may be rational numbers between the two convergents which are closer to x_0 than p_{k-1}/q_{k-1} and whose denominators are between q_k and q_{k-1}. Suppose k is odd. Since $x = q_k$, $y = p_k$ is one solution of $p_{k+1}x - q_{k+1}y = 1$, as we saw in the previous chapter, all the solutions are of the form $x = q_k + tq_{k+1}$, $y = p_k + tp_{k+1}$ for integers t.

Then, if we form the sequence of values of the ratio x/y for $t = 0,1,2, \cdots, a_{k+2}$, we get the sequence of fractions

$$\frac{p_k}{q_k}, \frac{p_k + p_{k+1}}{q_k + q_{k+1}}, \frac{p_k + 2p_{k+1}}{q_k + 2q_{k+1}}, \ldots, \frac{p_k + (a_{k+2} - 1)p_{k+1}}{q_k + (a_{k+2} - 1)q_{k+1}}, \frac{p_{k+2}}{q_{k+2}}.$$

It follows that k odd implies that p_k/q_k is less than x, and any rational a/b between p_k/q_k and x_0 must satisfy just one of the following three conditions: First, be one of the fractions in the sequence above; second, lie between one fraction and its successor; or, third, lie between the last fraction and x_0. In the third case, its denominator must be greater than q_{k+2}, since it lies between p_{k+2}/q_{k+2} and p_{k+1}/q_{k+1}. In the second case, its denominator must be greater than the denominator of the largest fraction in the above set to the left of which it lies. We call the sequence above the **intermediate convergents**. Notice that, if we consider the numerator the y-coordinate of a point and the denominator the x-coordinate, all these fractions represent points on the line $p_{k+1}x - q_{k+1}y = 1$.

· To obtain limits for the closeness of approximation of a convergent to the number, x_0, which the continued fraction represents, let x_{k+1} be the portion of the expansion of x beginning with a_{k+1}. Then, if a_{k+1} is replaced by x_{k+1} in

$$\frac{p_{k+1}}{q_{k+1}} = \frac{a_{k+1}p_k + p_{k-1}}{a_{k+1}q_k + q_{k-1}},$$

we will have an expression for x_0. From this it readily follows that

$$x_0 - \frac{p_k}{q_k} = \frac{(-1)^{k-1}}{q_k(x_{k+1}q_k + q_{k-1})}.$$

Furthermore, $x_{k+1}q_k + q_{k-1} \geqq a_{k+1}q_k + q_{k-1} = q_{k+1} > q_k$, the inequality holding in the first instance unless x is a rational number whose expansion terminates with a_{k+1}. Furthermore,

$$q_{k-1} = q_{k+1} - a_{k+1}q_k$$

implies

$$x_{k+1}q_k + q_{k-1} = (x_{k+1} - a_{k+1})q_k + q_{k+1} < q_k + q_{k+1} < 2q_{k+1}.$$

Combining all these results, we have

Theorem 4.6b. If p_k/q_k are convergents of the continued-fraction expansion of x, then

$$\frac{1}{2q_kq_{k+1}} < \frac{1}{q_k(q_k + q_{k+1})} \leqq \left| x - \frac{p_k}{q_k} \right| \leqq \frac{1}{q_kq_{k+1}} < \frac{1}{q_k^2}.$$

It is not hard to see that the equalities cannot hold if x is irrational, but there are values of x making the following differences arbitrarily small:

$$\frac{1}{q_kq_{k+1}} - \left| x - \frac{p_k}{q_k} \right|, \quad \left| x - \frac{p_k}{q_k} \right| - \frac{1}{q_k(q_k + q_{k+1})}.$$

Furthermore, the larger the q_k, the closer the approximation.

Exercises 4.6

1. In the manner described above, plot on a graph the first three convergents of $\sqrt{17}$ and the intermediate convergents.

2. Similarly, plot the first three convergents and the intermediate convergents of π.

3. Fill in the details of the proof of Theorem 4.6b.

4. Find values of x and k for which one of the differences at the end of Section 4.6 is less than .01. Would there be a value of x for which both differences would be less than .01 for all k beyond a certain value?

5. From Theorem 4.6b how close must the third convergents in Exercises 1 and 2 be to the true value?

6. Prove that $(x - p_k/q_k)/(x - p_{k-1}/q_{k-1}) = -q_{k-1}/q_k x_{k+1}$.

7. Using continued fractions, find $\sqrt[3]{4}$ accurate to three decimal places.

8. If a/b and c/d are two fractions in lowest terms for which a,b,c,d are positive integers and $bc - ad > 1$, show that there are two positive integers r and s with $s < d$ and $cs - rd = 1$. Show that this implies

$$a/b < r/s < c/d.$$

9. The so-called **Farey Sequence** of order 5 is the set of rational numbers in order which are between 0 and 1 in value and whose denominators are not greater than 5, that is,

$$0, 1/5, 1/4, 1/3, 2/5, 1/2, 3/5, 2/3, 3/4, 4/5, 1.$$

Show that if a/b and c/d are any two successive fractions of a Farey Sequence of any order then $cb - ad = 1$. In this connection the results of Exercise 8 above are useful. (Ref. 6, pp. 23 ff.)

4.7. Expansions of quadratic surds

We saw in Chapter II that every rational number has a periodic decimal expansion; that is, from a certain point on, the same sequence of digits recurs again and again without ceasing. This includes the case when the expansion ends with a succession of zeros. Similarly a periodic continued fraction is defined to be one in which, from a certain point on, there is a sequence of values of the a_i which repeats again and again without ceasing. This definition excludes finite continued fractions, which represent rational numbers. It is a remarkable property of continued fractions that every periodic continued fraction represents an irrational root of a quadratic equation with integer coefficients and, conversely, every irrational (and hence real) root of a quadratic equation with integer coefficients has a periodic continued-fraction expansion. We first have

Theorem 4.7a. Any periodic continued fraction represents a root of a quadratic equation with integer coefficients.

Since the proof is not difficult, we give here merely an outline leaving the details to the student. As above, let x_k denote that part of the expansion beginning with a_k. If the expansion is periodic, then for some k and r, the portion beginning with a_r is equal to the portion beginning with a_k. This shows that, for some k and r, the following equality holds: $x_k = x_r$. Take $r < k$ and let p'_i/q'_i denote the convergents of x_r. Then we have

$$x_r = \frac{p'_{k-r-1}x_k - p'_{k-r-2}}{q'_{k-r-1}x_k - q'_{k-r-2}} = x_k,$$

which shows that x_k satisfies a quadratic equation with integer coefficients. Then $x = (p_{k-1}x_k + p_{k-2})/(q_{k-1}x_k + q_{k-2})$ shows that x likewise satisfies a quadratic equation with integer coefficients.

It is somewhat harder to prove the converse of this theorem, that is

Theorem 4.7b. If x is an irrational root of a quadratic equation,

$$ax^2 + bx + c = 0,$$

where a, b, and c are integers, then its continued-fraction expansion is periodic.

As above, we see that

$$x = (x_k p_{k-1} + p_{k-2})/(x_k q_{k-1} + q_{k-2}).$$

To simplify our notation, replace $x_k, p_{k-1}, p_{k-2}, q_{k-1}, q_{k-2}$ by z, r, s, t, u, respectively, and have

(1) $$x = \frac{rz + s}{tz + u}, \qquad |ru - ts| = 1.$$

Then, by Theorem 4.6b, we have

$$x = r/t + \epsilon/t^2 = s/u + \eta/u^2, \ |\epsilon| < 1 > |\eta|,$$

since if $x - p_{k-1}/q_{k-1}$ (that is, $x - r/t$) is less in absolute value than $1/q_{k-1}^2$ it must be $1/q_{k-1}^2$ (that is, $1/t^2$) multiplied by a number, ϵ, less than 1 in absolute value. A similar statement is true for $x - p_{k-2}/q_{k-2}$. If we substitute in $ax^2 + bx + c = 0$ the value for x given in (1), we get $Az^2 + Bz + C = 0$, where

$$A = ar^2 + brt + ct^2,$$
$$B = 2ars + b(ru + ts) + 2ctu,$$
$$C = as^2 + bsu + cu^2.$$

Now, if we can show that $A, B,$ and C are bounded, that is, must be less in absolute value than some fixed number independent of x_k, or z, and depending only on x, then, since they are integers, there is only a finite number of different equations which z can satisfy. However, the continued fraction does not stop, since x is irrational. This fact would show that two such equations must be identical and hence two values of z are the same. As soon as a value of z recurs, the continued fraction repeats. Therefore the rest of the proof consists in showing that $A, B,$ and C are bounded.

Now,

$$A/t^2 = a(r/t)^2 + b(r/t) + c,$$
$$= a(x - \epsilon/t^2)^2 + b(x - \epsilon/t^2) + c,$$
$$= ax^2 + bx + c - 2a\epsilon x/t^2 + a\epsilon^2/t^4 - b\epsilon/t^2.$$

Thus, since $ax^2 + bx + c = 0$, we have

$$A = -2a\epsilon x + a\epsilon^2/t^2 - b\epsilon,$$
$$|A| \leq |2ax| + |a| + |b|,$$

which is bounded. Using s/u in place of r/t, we see that C is bounded.

To complete the proof, one may proceed in either of two directions. First, it may be shown by direct computation, in virtue of the values of $A, B,$ and C given above, that $4AC - B^2 = 4ac - b^2$. This is straightforward but rather long. However, it does show that, once A and C are determined, then B is determined except for sign.

Second, it may be shown directly, as follows, that B is bounded. By the same method as that above, the reader may easily find that

$$B = -(\epsilon u/t + \eta t/u)(2ax + b) + 2a\epsilon\eta/tu.$$

Since r/t and s/u are successive convergents of the continued fraction, expansion of x, ϵ, and η are of opposite signs, a fact which shows

$$|\epsilon u/t + \eta t/u| \leq |\epsilon u/t - \eta t/u|.$$

However, $x = r/t + \epsilon/t^2 = s/u + \eta/u^2$ implies $(-ru + st)/tu = \epsilon/t^2 - \eta/u^2$, and hence $|\epsilon u/t - \eta t/u| = |ru - st| = 1$, which shows

$$|B| \leq |2ax + b| + |2a|,$$

and is therefore bounded.

Exercises 4.7

1. Fill in the details of the proof of Theorem 4.7a.

2. Verify by computation that $4AC - B^2 = 4ac - b^2$ in the last proof.

3. Making use of the fact verified in Exercise 2, prove that if $x^2 - D = 0$ where D is a positive integer, the number of equations which the accompanying z may satisfy is not more than $2(2\sqrt{D} + 1)^2$ and hence that the repeating portion of the continued-fraction expansion of $\sqrt{D}$ contains no more than $2(2\sqrt{D} + 1)^2$ terms. As a matter of fact, this estimate has been considerably improved. (The maximum is $d(2d + 1)$, d being the greatest integer in $\sqrt{D}$, Ref. 15, p. 34.)

4. Find the continued-fraction expansions of $\sqrt{7}, \sqrt{11}, \sqrt{13}$. Compare them with those already found for $\sqrt{3}, \sqrt{5}, \sqrt{17}$. Can you find any properties common to all these expansions?

5. Show that

$$\begin{vmatrix} a & b \\ c & d \end{vmatrix} \cdot \begin{vmatrix} a' & b' \\ c' & d' \end{vmatrix} = \begin{vmatrix} aa' + bc' & ab' + bd' \\ ca' + dc' & cb' + dd' \end{vmatrix},$$

noticing the element in the first row and column of the product of the determinants is the sum of the products of corresponding elements in the first row of the left determinant and first column of the right determinant. Similarly, the element in the first row and second column of the product is obtained by multiplying elements of the first row of the left determinant and the second column of the right determinant. Show that the correct values for A, B, and C satisfy

$$\begin{vmatrix} r & t \\ s & u \end{vmatrix} \cdot \begin{vmatrix} 2a & b \\ b & 2c \end{vmatrix} \cdot \begin{vmatrix} r & s \\ t & u \end{vmatrix} = \begin{vmatrix} 2A & B \\ B & 2C \end{vmatrix}.$$

Use this result to show that $4ac - b^2 = 4AC - B^2$.

6. Show that whenever the continued-fraction expansion for x is "pure periodic," that is, if the repeating portion begins with the first term, then if k is the length of the period we have

$$x = (p_k x + p_{k-1})/(q_k x + q_{k-1}).$$

Hence show that if $x = \sqrt{D}$ has a pure periodic continued-fraction expansion and D is a positive rational number, then $p_k = q_{k-1}$, $p_{k-1}/q_k = D$, and

$$p_k^2 - Dq_k^2 = \pm 1.$$

7. Show that D in Exercise 6 cannot be an integer.

4.8. Pure periodicity and reduced quadratic surds

The remainder of this chapter will be primarily concerned with developing a method of solution of the **Pell Equation**

$$x^2 - Dy^2 = 1,$$

where D is a positive integer, not a perfect square. Though the equation bears his name, Pell apparently did not contribute to its solution. Exercise 6 above gave a preview of the kind of connection to be expected. However, as was shown, it does not apply for D an integer. To find a solution for D an integer we first need more information about the form of the continued-fraction expansion of $\sqrt{D}$. We shall first need to characterize the numbers x whose continued-fraction expansions are pure periodic; that is,

$$x = (a_1, a_2, \cdots, a_k, a_1, a_2, \cdots, a_k, \cdots).$$

As in Exercise 6 above, we then have

$$q_k x^2 + (q_{k-1} - p_k)x - p_{k-1} = 0.$$

Since the quadratic expression has the value $-p_{k-1}$ when $x = 0$ and $q_k + p_k - q_{k-1} - p_{k-1}$ when $x = -1$, the latter being positive and the former being negative, we see that the equation has a root between 0 and -1. That is, the other root of the quadratic equation which x

satisfies, in brief, the **conjugate** of x, lies between 0 and -1. We then call a positive root of a quadratic equation with integer coefficients a **reduced quadratic surd** if it is greater than 1 and if its conjugate lies between 0 and -1. We have thus proved the "only if" part of the following theorem.

Theorem 4.8. A number x has a pure periodic continued-fraction expansion if and only if it is a reduced quadratic surd.

To complete the proof we must show that any reduced quadratic surd x has a pure periodic continued-fraction expansion. First, we need to show that if x is a reduced quadratic surd, then x_2 is also, if x_2 is defined by the equation $x = a_1 + 1/x_2$. If we let y be the conjugate of x, then the conjugate of x_2, which we may call y_2, is defined by the equation $y = a_1 + 1/y_2$, for if $f(x) = 0$ is the equation for x, the equation for x_2 is $f(a_1 + 1/x_2)$, and $f(y) = 0$ shows that the equation for y_2 is $f(a_1 + 1/y_2)$; hence y_2 and x_2 satisfy the same quadratic equation. However, $y - 1/y_2 = a_1 \geq 1$ and $y < 0$ implies $-1 < y_2 < 0$, which shows that x_2 is a reduced quadratic surd. Hence by continuing this process we see that if x is a reduced quadratic surd, so is x_k for every k.

Let $x = (a_1, a_2, \cdots, a_r, a_{r+1}, \cdots, a_{r+k}, a_{r+k+1}, \cdots)$, where the repeating portion is $a_{r+1}, \cdots, a_{r+k}$. Now $y_r = a_r + 1/y_{r+1}$ implies $-1/y_{r+1} = a_r - y_r$, and, since $0 < -y_r < 1$, we have

$$a_r = [-1/y_{r+1}],$$

the square bracket denoting the greatest integer in $-1/y_{r+1}$. Similarly, $y_{k+r} = a_{k+r} + 1/y_{k+r+1}$ implies $a_{k+r} = [-1/y_{k+r+1}]$. However, $x_{r+1} = x_{r+k+1}$ implies $y_{r+1} = y_{r+k+1}$, which implies that the greatest integers in the negative reciprocals of the last two quantities are equal, that is, $a_r = a_{r+k}$. Similarly, we may show that $a_{r-1} = a_{r+k-1}$ and so on back to a_1. This completes the proof.

We leave to the student the proof of the

Corollary 4.8. The continued-fraction expansion of $\sqrt{D}$, where D is a positive integer, not a perfect square, is of the form

$$(a_1, a_2, a_3, \cdots, a_k, a_{k+1}, a_2, a_3, \cdots),$$

where the repeating part is that portion from a_2 to a_{k+1} inclusive.

4.9. The Pell Equation

We can now prove

Theorem 4.9a. If D is a positive integer which is not a perfect square and such that the continued-fraction expansion of $\sqrt{D}$ has a repeating portion of k terms, then p_k, q_k is a solution of

$$(1) \qquad\qquad x^2 - Dy^2 = (-1)^k.$$

To prove this notice that $x_2 = x_{k+2}$ implies

$$x = (x_{k+2}p_{k+1} + p_k)/(x_{k+2}q_{k+1} + q_k) = (x_2 p_{k+1} + p_k)/(x_2 q_{k+1} + q_k).$$

However, $x = \sqrt{D}$ implies that $x_2 = 1/(\sqrt{D} - a_1)$, and substitution in the above displayed equation gives us

$$\sqrt{D} = \frac{p_{k+1} + p_k(\sqrt{D} - a_1)}{q_{k+1} + q_k(\sqrt{D} - a_1)},$$

which results in the equation

$$q_k D + \sqrt{D}(q_{k+1} - a_1 q_k) = p_{k+1} + p_k(\sqrt{D} - a_1).$$

Equating the rational and irrational parts gives the equations

$$(2) \qquad\qquad q_{k+1} - a_1 q_k - p_k = 0,$$
$$p_{k+1} - a_1 p_k - q_k D = 0.$$

Eliminating a_1 by multiplying the first equation by $-p_k$ and the second by q_k, and adding, gives

$$-p_k q_{k+1} + q_k p_{k+1} + p_k^2 - Dq_k^2 = 0,$$

which results in our theorem.

We have just shown that a properly chosen convergent of the continued fraction expansion of $\sqrt{D}$ gives a solution of equation (1). We shall now show that every solution of

$$x^2 - Dy^2 = \pm 1 \; ; x, y \text{ positive},$$

is given by a convergent of the continued fraction for $\sqrt{D}$. More precisely, we have

Theorem 4.9b. If p/q is a solution of one of the equations

$$x^2 - Dy^2 = \pm 1,$$

with p and q relatively prime positive integers, then p/q is a convergent in the continued-fraction expansion of $\sqrt{D}$.

Now, $p^2 - Dq^2 = 1$ implies

$$|p/q - \sqrt{D}| = 1/(p + q\sqrt{D})q < 1/2q^2, \text{ if } D > 3.$$

Hence, except for $D = 2,3$, the above theorem will be an immediate consequence of

Theorem 4.9c. If $|r/s - x| < 1/2s^2$ and r and s are relatively prime positive integers, then r/s is a convergent of the continued-fraction expansion of x.

To prove this, let the continued-fraction expansion of r/s with k odd be $(a_1, a_2, \cdots, a_k)$, and let x_{k+1} be defined by the finite continued fraction

$$x = (a_1, a_2, \cdots, a_k, x_{k+1}).$$

If x_{k+1} is not less than 1, we can expand it into a continued fraction and we will have a continued-fraction expansion of x, which, in virtue of its uniqueness, is *the* continued fraction for x. Hence we need only show that x_{k+1} so defined is not less than 1.

Now, $x = (p_k x_{k+1} + p_{k-1})/(q_k x_{k+1} + q_{k-1})$ may be solved for x_{k+1}, giving

$$(1) \qquad x_{k+1} = \frac{q_{k-1}x - p_{k-1}}{-q_k x + p_k}.$$

However, $p_k/q_k = r/s$ and the hypothesis of our theorem tells us that

$$|x - p_k/q_k| < 1/2q_k^2.$$

Now, k odd implies that x is greater than p_k/q_k, and hence we may write

$$x - p_k/q_k = \epsilon < 1/2q_k^2.$$

Solving the equation for x, substituting in (1) and simplifying, we get

$$x_{k+1} = (1 - \epsilon q_k q_{k-1})/\epsilon q_k^2,$$

which is not less than 1 if $1 - \epsilon q_k q_{k-1} \geqq \epsilon q_k^2$, that is, $\epsilon(q_k^2 + q_k q_{k-1}) \leqq 1$. However, $\epsilon < 1/2q_k^2$ and $q_{k-1} < q_k$ implies

$$\epsilon(q_k^2 + q_k q_{k-1}) < (q_k^2 + q_k q_{k-1})/2q_k^2 < (q_k^2 + q_k^2)/2q_k^2 = 1,$$

which proves our result.

Exercises 4.9

1. Prove Corollary 4.8.

2. Have we shown that the least positive solution of

$$x^2 - Dy^2 = 1,$$

that is, the solution in positive integers for which y is the least, is given by the kth convergent in the expansion of $\sqrt{D}$, where k is the number of terms in the period?

3. Would Theorem 4.9c necessarily hold if the inequality were replaced by "less than or equal to"?

4. Using expansions found in the previous set of exercises, find solutions of the equations

$$x^2 - Dy^2 = \pm 1$$

for $D = 3,5,17,7,11,13$.

5. Show that Theorem 4.9b holds also for $D = 2$, $D = 3$.

6. Show that if $D \equiv 3 \pmod 4$, the equation

$$x^2 - Dy^2 = -1$$

has no solution.

7. By use of exercise 6 or other means, show that if $D \equiv 3 \pmod 4$ the number of terms in the periodic part of the expansion of $\sqrt{D}$ must be even.

8. Show that if r,s is a solution of

$$x^2 - Dy^2 = \pm 1,$$

with D an integer, not a perfect square, then the integers r_n, s_n, defined by

$$(r + s\sqrt{D})^n = r_n + \sqrt{D}s_n,$$

n an integer, is a solution of

$$x^2 - Dy^2 = (\pm 1)^n,$$

where the ambiguous signs correspond.

9. Use the result of Exercise 8 to find a solution of

$$x^2 - 17y^2 = 1$$

from the solution 4,1 of the corresponding equation, with -1 on the right side.

10. In Exercise 8 is it necessary for any or all of r,s,n to be *positive* integers? Would the result hold if D were a perfect square?

11. Would the result of Exercise 8 hold if D were a negative integer? If so, of what help would it be?

4.10. Further information about the Pell Equation

Though we have at hand all the machinery for dealing with the Pell Equation, there are two additional refinements which are of interest.

First, we have not shown that the smallest positive solution of $x^2 - Dy^2 = \pm 1$ (that is, the solution in positive integers for which y is the least, choosing ± 1 to be -1 if there is a solution for this choice, otherwise choosing ± 1 to be 1) is the kth convergent, where k is the number of terms in the periodic part. From a computational point of view, this information is not necessary, since one would use the first convergent which gave a solution, but it would free us from trying any until we reach the kth term. Hence we shall prove

Theorem 4.10a. If the rth convergent of $\sqrt{D}$ gives a solution of

$$x^2 - Dy^2 = \pm 1,$$

then r is divisible by k, the number of terms in the period of the expansion of $\sqrt{D}$.

Suppose we show that $x_{r+2} = x_2$ whenever the rth convergent of $\sqrt{D}$ gives a solution of the Pell Equation. Then, if P,Q is the least pair of positive integers such that $P^2 - DQ^2 = \pm 1$, P/Q will be a convergent of the expansion of $\sqrt{D}$ by Theorem 4.9b. Call it the Rth convergent, and have $x_{R+2} = x_2$. Then $k = R$, since if k were less than R, Theorem 4.9a would show that the Pell Equation would have a smaller solution than P,Q. Then $x_{r+2} = x_2$ would imply r divisible by k. It thus remains to show that $x_{r+2} = x_2$, whenever the rth convergent of $\sqrt{D}$ gives a solution of the Pell Equation. Notice that $\pm 1 = (-1)^r$, since p_r/q_r is less than $\sqrt{D}$ if r is odd and greater if r is even.

Now, $\sqrt{D} = x = (p_r x_{r+1} + p_{r-1})/(q_r x_{r+1} + q_{r-1})$ shows that

$$(p_r - \sqrt{D}q_r)x_{r+1} = -p_{r-1} + \sqrt{D}q_{r-1}.$$

Multiplying both sides by $p_r + \sqrt{D}q_r$ and making use of the fact that $p_r^2 - Dq_r^2 = (-1)^r$ we get

$$x_{r+1} = (-1)^r \{Dq_r q_{r-1} - p_r p_{r-1} + \sqrt{D}(p_r q_{r-1} - q_r p_{r-1})\}$$
$$= \sqrt{D} + (-1)^r (Dq_r q_{r-1} - p_r p_{r-1}),$$

which implies that

$$x_{r+1} = a_{r+1} + \sqrt{D} - a_1, \text{ where } a_{r+1} = (-1)^r (Dq_r q_{r-1} - p_r p_{r-1}) + a_1.$$

Now, $x_{r+1} = a_{r+1} + 1/x_{r+2}$, where, from the line above,

$$1/x_{r+2} = \sqrt{D} - a_1 = 1/x_2;$$

thus $x_2 = x_{r+2}$, which was to be proved.

There is a certain interesting symmetry about the continued-fraction expansion of $\sqrt{D}$, which is quite easy to find. The reader may have observed that the first $k - 1$ terms of the periodic part are symmetric about the middle. So we shall demonstrate

Theorem 4.10b. The continued-fraction expansion of $\sqrt{D}$, where D is a positive integer, not a square, is of the form

$$(a_1, a_2, a_3, a_4, \cdots, a_4, a_3, a_2, 2a_1, \cdots),$$

where the periodic part consists of all the terms exhibited except the first.

From the first of equations (2) in the proof of Theorem 4.9a we have

$$q_{k+1}/q_k = a_1 + p_k/q_k.$$

However, $q_{k+1} = a_{k+1}q_k + q_{k-1}$ implies $q_{k+1}/q_k = a_{k+1} + q_{k-1}/q_k$ (compare Exercise 5, section 4.4). Hence $a_{k+1} = [q_{k-1}/q_k]$, since $q_{k-1} < q_k$. Continuing this process, we have

$$\frac{q_{k+1}}{q_k} = a_{k+1} + \frac{1}{q_k/q_{k-1}} = a_{k+1} + \frac{1}{a_k + \cdots},$$

and hence

$$q_{k+1}/q_k = (a_{k+1}, a_k, a_{k-1}, \cdots, a_2).$$

However,

$$a_1 + p_k/q_k = (2a_1, a_2, a_3, \cdots, a_k),$$

and the equality of the two quantities on the left shows that

$$a_{k+1} = 2a_1, a_2 = a_k, a_3 = a_{k-1}, \cdots.$$

Thus the theorem is proved.

While the computation of the kth convergent of $\sqrt{D}$ is not very difficult to accomplish, there is a quicker way to find other solutions of the Pell Equation, as was suggested in Exercise 8 of the previous section. We have

Theorem 4.10c. If p,q is the smallest positive integral solution of the Pell Equation, all positive integral solutions p_n,q_n are given by the formula

$$(p + q\sqrt{D})^n = p_n + \sqrt{D}q_n.$$

To prove this, suppose that r,s is a positive solution. Then $r + s\sqrt{D}$ will lie between two successive powers of $p + q\sqrt{D}$. That is, for some positive integer m, the following inequalities hold:

$$(p + q\sqrt{D})^m \leq r + s\sqrt{D} \leq (p + q\sqrt{D})^{m+1}.$$

Letting $(p + q\sqrt{D})^m = p_m + q_m\sqrt{D}$ and dividing through by this quantity, we have

(1) $$1 \leq t + u\sqrt{D} \leq p + q\sqrt{D},$$

where

$$t + u\sqrt{D} = (r + s\sqrt{D})/(p_m + q_m\sqrt{D}) = (r + s\sqrt{D})(p_m - q_m\sqrt{D}),$$

the second equality following from Exercise 8 of Section 4.9, and

$$t = rp_m - sq_mD, u = p_ms - q_mr.$$

Replacing $\sqrt{D}$ by $-\sqrt{D}$ in the above, we get

$$t - u\sqrt{D} = (r - s\sqrt{D})(p_m + q_m\sqrt{D}).$$

Multiplying corresponding sides, we have

$$t^2 - Du^2 = (r^2 - Ds^2)(p_m^2 - q_m^2D) - 1.$$

Suppose t and u are positive. Then

$$t^2 = 1 + Du^2, p^2 = 1 + Dq^2$$

would show that either $t > p$ and $u > q$ or else $t < p$ and $u < q$. Inequalities (1) then imply that the latter holds, which denies our supposition that p,q is the smallest positive solution. Thus, to complete our proof we need only show that t and u are positive. Now,

(2) $$p_m^2 - q_m^2D = 1 = r^2 - Ds^2$$

implies $r > s\sqrt{D}$, $p_m > q_m\sqrt{D}$ and hence $t > 0$. Also u has the same sign as $(p_ms - q_mr)(p_ms + q_mr)$, which is equal to $p_m^2s^2 - q_m^2r^2$. However, (2) implies $p_m^2s^2 = s^2 + q_m^2s^2D$, $q_m^2r^2 = q_m^2 + Ds^2q_m^2$, and hence u has the same sign as

$$(3) \qquad\qquad p_m^2s^2 - q_m^2r^2 = s^2 - q_m^2 = (r^2 - p_m^2)/D.$$

However, $p_m + q_m\sqrt{D} < r + s\sqrt{D}$ implies either $p_m < r$ or $q_m < s$. In the former case, the second equality of (3) shows that u is positive; in the latter case the first equality of (3) shows that u is positive.

Using this theorem, we can find all solutions of the Pell Equation by finding the least positive one by continued fractions and Theorem 4.10c to find all the rest.

Exercises 4.10

1. If the length of the period of the expansion of $\sqrt{D}$ is odd, what will be the simplest way to find the least positive solution of the Pell Equation?

2. The equation $x^2 - Dy^2 = 1$ represents an hyperbola. Draw a graph showing the relationship of the solutions of the Pell Equation to the hyperbola.

3. Show that if $x^2 - Dy^2 = -1$ is solvable and p,q is its smallest solution, then all positive integral solutions p_n, q_n of $|x^2 - Dy^2| = 1$ are given by

$$(p + q\sqrt{D})^n = p_n + \sqrt{D}q_n,$$

and that $p_n^2 - Dq_n^2 = (-1)^n$.

Nonlinear Congruences

5.1. Introduction

Just as in algebra we consider roots of equations $f(x) = 0$, here we are concerned with the congruence

$$f(x) \equiv 0 \ (\text{mod } m),$$

where $f(x)$ is a polynomial with integral coefficients. Sometimes we might want to know the roots and at other times we would be satisfied to know the number of roots. Of course, in the latter instance we mean the number of incongruent roots (mod m).

We have already found that some linear congruences have no roots, some have one, and some have many. However, if the modulus is a prime, the situation is more satisfactory, since each linear congruence, where the coefficient of x is prime to the modulus, has exactly one solution. We shall find that for congruences of higher degree and prime modulus, the theory is also quite satisfactory.

Exercises 5.1

1. Show that a congruence $x^2 \equiv a \ (\text{mod } p)$ has two solutions or none if p is a prime and $a \not\equiv 0 \ (\text{mod } p)$. Find integers a and m for which $x^2 \equiv a$ (mod m) has more than two solutions.

2. List some of the important theorems in the theory of equations, guess whether or not they hold for congruences, test your guesses by examples,

and then see if you can prove them. One such theorem would be the remainder theorem.

5.2.   The remainder theorem

The reader will recall that in algebra conditional equations and identical equations were discussed. A polynomial $f(x)$ was defined to be identically equal to zero if, after terms were collected, the coefficient of each power of x was zero. A second definition reads: A polynomial $f(x)$ is identically equal to zero if $f(x) = 0$ for all values of x. These two definitions are equivalent for polynomials whose coefficients are complex numbers, since no such polynomial equation can have more roots than its degree unless all coefficients of x are zero. However, the definitions are not equivalent for congruence, as can be seen by the example

$$x^5 - x \equiv 0 \pmod{5},$$

which is satisfied for each value of x (mod 5), though the coefficients of not all the powers of x are divisible by 5. In fact,

$$5x^5 - 5x \equiv 0 \pmod{25}$$

has 25 roots.

Since we have used three horizontal lines for congruence, we shall use four for identical congruence when we wish to emphasize identity. Thus we write

$$f(x) \equiv\!\equiv 0 \pmod{m}$$

only if each coefficient of $f(x)$ is divisible by m, and, similarly,

$$f(x) \equiv\!\equiv g(x) \pmod{m}$$

when $f(x)$ and $g(x)$ are two polynomials with the property that the coefficient of each power of x in $f(x)$ is congruent (mod m) to the corresponding coefficient in $g(x)$. For example, we would write

$$5x^3 - x^2 + 2x - 1 \equiv\!\equiv 4(x + 4)^2 \pmod{5},$$

but

$$x^5 \not\equiv\!\equiv x \pmod{5},$$

since in the latter case corresponding coefficients are not congruent (mod 5). Strictly speaking, perhaps, we should also write

$$6 \equiv 1 \ (\text{mod } 5),$$

but we customarily omit the fourth line when only numbers are involved, since such omission will cause no confusion. Using our notation, $f(x) \equiv 0$ (mod m) implies that $f(a) \equiv 0$ (mod m) for all integers a, but $f(a) \equiv 0$ (mod m) for all integers a does not imply $f(x) \equiv 0$ (mod m).

We showed in the theory of equations that if $f(x)$ is a polynomial in x and if, when it is divided by $(x - a)$, the quotient is $q(x)$ and the remainder is R, then it may be written in the form

(1) $$f(x) \equiv (x - a)q(x) + R,$$

and $R = f(a)$. This was called the remainder theorem. The corresponding result for congruences is expressed in

Theorem 5.2. (The remainder theorem.) If $f(x)$ is a polynomial such that

(2) $$f(x) \equiv (x - a)q(x) + R \ (\text{mod } m),$$

then $R \equiv f(a)$ (mod m).

To prove this, notice that the identity (1) implies the identical congruence (2) which must hold for all integer values of x. If we then replace x by a we get the desired result.

5.3. The number of roots of a congruence

We have seen examples of congruences which have more roots than their degree, for example, $x^2 \equiv 1$ (mod 8) whose roots are 1,3,5,7. However, if the modulus is a prime number, we have

Theorem 5.3a. If $f(x)$ is a polynomial of degree n, the congruence

$$f(x) \equiv 0 \ (\text{mod } p)$$

has no more than n distinct roots, p being a prime number.

Suppose the congruence has a root a. Then $f(a) \equiv 0$ (mod p), and the remainder theorem shows that

$$f(x) \equiv (x - a)q(x) \ (\text{mod } p).$$

If b is another root, $f(b) \equiv 0 \pmod{p}$ implies $(b - a)q(b) \equiv 0 \pmod{p}$. Then $b \not\equiv a \pmod{p}$ implies $q(b) \equiv 0 \pmod{p}$. Thus, by the remainder theorem, $q(x) \equiv (x - b)r(x) \pmod{p}$. Continuing in this fashion, we see that each root leads to a linear factor, and, since there can be no more than n linear factors, our proof is complete.

There are theorems for moduli which are powers of primes (Ref. 10, pp. 85–90), but they are too complex for inclusion here. We leave as an exercise the proof of the following theorem.

Theorem 5.3b. Let $f(x)$ be a polynomial of degree n less than p, where p is an odd prime, and suppose

$$x^p - x \equiv f(x)q(x) + r(x), \ r(x) \text{ of degree } < n.$$

Then $f(x) \equiv 0 \pmod{p}$ has n distinct roots if and only if $r(x) \equiv 0 \pmod{p}$. If $f(0) \not\equiv 0 \pmod{p}$, $x^p - x$ may be replaced by $x^{p-1} - 1$ above.

Exercises 5.3

1. Is the following true? Suppose $a \not\equiv 0 \pmod{m}$. Then if $ax^2 + bx + c \equiv 0 \pmod{m}$ has one root, it has two? If your answer is "yes," prove it; if "no," give an example. Would your conclusions be the same if the modulus were a prime?

2. A polynomial equation of odd degree with real coefficients must have at least one real root. Give an example of a cubic congruence with no roots.

3. Where does the proof of Theorem 5.3a break down when p is not a prime number? Does the theorem hold for a power of a prime?

4. Show that $x^2 \equiv a \pmod{p}$ has two roots or none if a is not divisible by p (p being an odd prime), and hence there are $(p - 1)/2$ values of a for which $x^2 \equiv a \pmod{p}$ has a solution. If the congruence is solvable, a is called a **quadratic residue** of p; if not, a **nonresidue.**

5. If R is a quadratic residue of p and N a quadratic nonresidue, show that RN is a quadratic nonresidue for p an odd prime.

6. Let $R_1, R_2, \cdots, R_k$, $k = (p - 1)/2$, be the quadratic residues of an odd prime p, and N a quadratic nonresidue. Show that $NR_1, NR_2, \cdots,$

NR_k are the quadratic nonresidues. Show that if N_1 and N_2 are any two nonresidues, the congruence $N_1 x^2 \equiv N_2 \pmod{p}$ is solvable.

7. Using Fermat's Theorem, show that

$$x^{p-1} - 1 \equiv (x - 1)(x - 2) \cdots (x - p + 1) \equiv 0 \pmod{p}$$

of degree $p - 2$ has $p - 1$ roots and hence, by Theorem 5.3a, has all its coefficients divisible by p, p being an odd prime. Show that this implies Wilson's Theorem. See Sections 2.5 and 2.11.

8. Prove Theorem 5.3b.

9. In a manner analogous to the definition of $i = \sqrt{-1}$, define for a given prime p and a quadratic nonresidue N, a number j such that $j^2 = N$. Show that every quadratic congruence $x^2 + bx + c \equiv 0 \pmod{p}$ has a solution of the form $r + sj$, where r and s are integers. HINT: Write $x^2 + bx + c = (x + b/2)^2 + c - b^2/4$ and see that $-c + b^2/4 \equiv r^2 \pmod{p}$ for some integer r, or else, using Exercise 6, $-c + b^2/4 \equiv Nr^2 \equiv j^2 r^2 \pmod{p}$ for some r.

10. Show that $x^3 \equiv 2 \pmod{7}$ has no solution of the form $r + sj$, where r and s are integers and j is defined so that $j^2 \equiv 3 \pmod{7}$.

11. Show how the solutions of the congruence $f(x) \equiv 0 \pmod{m}$ could be obtained from the solutions for the prime power factors of m.

12. Show that $ax^2 + by^2 \equiv c \pmod{p}$ is solvable if $(ab,p) = 1$. See Exercise 8 of Section 2.5.

5.4. Power residues

The above exercises show that not much of the usual theory of equations carries over to the solution of polynomial congruences in number theory. Perhaps this was to be expected, for we noticed in the beginning that the problem of divisibility which is trivial for real numbers is a matter of concern in the theory of numbers. So the solution of $x^2 = a$ in complex numbers is always possible, but the corresponding congruence $\pmod{p}$ often has no solution. A definite criterion is given by

Theorem 5.4. If p is a prime and $(p,a) = 1$ the congruence

$$x^n \equiv a \pmod{p}$$

is solvable if and only if $a^e \equiv 1 \pmod{p}$, where e is defined by $(p-1)/e = (n, p-1)$. When it is solvable there are $(p-1)/e$ solutions.

We postpone until later the proof for all n, being content for the present with the cases when n is a divisor of $p-1$ or when $a = 1$. In the first case n, a divisor of $(p-1)$, implies $(n, p-1) = n$ and $ne = p-1$. Then, if we notice that $x^{ne} - a^e$ is divisible by $x^n - a$, we can write

$$x^{ne} - a^e \equiv (x^n - a)q(x),$$

where $q(x)$ is a polynomial with integer coefficients. Hence

$$x^{p-1} - 1 \equiv x^{ne} - a^e + a^e - 1 \equiv (x^n - a)q(x) + a^e - 1.$$

If $x^n - a \equiv 0 \pmod{p}$ has any solution x_0, Fermat's Theorem and the above identity show that

$$(x_0^n - a)q(x_0) + a^e - 1 \equiv x_0^{p-1} - 1 \equiv 0 \pmod{p},$$

and hence

$$a^e - 1 \equiv 0 \pmod{p}.$$

Conversely, if the last congruence holds, Theorem 5.3b shows that

$$x^n - a \equiv 0 \pmod{p}$$

has n solutions. This completes the proof for the case when n divides $p-1$.

We can also prove the theorem when $a = 1$ without restricting n to be a divisor of $p-1$. To do this, let $k = (n, p-1)$. We know that there are integers r and s such that $nr + (p-1)s = k$. Then $x_0^n \equiv 1 \pmod{p}$ and $x_0^{p-1} \equiv 1 \pmod{p}$ imply

$$x_0^{nr + (p-1)s} \equiv x_0^k \equiv 1 \pmod{p}.$$

Conversely, if k divides n and $x_0^k \equiv 1 \pmod{p}$, it follows that $x_0^n \equiv 1 \pmod{p}$. What we proved in the preceding paragraph then shows that there are k solutions of $x^k \equiv 1 \pmod{p}$. Hence the number of solutions of $x^n \equiv 1 \pmod{p}$ is k, which is equal to $(p-1)/e$.

Exercises 5.4

1. If $p \equiv 1 \pmod{3}$, show that $x^3 \equiv a \pmod{p}$ has 3 or no solutions for $(p, a) = 1$. Where there are solutions, express them in the form $x_0, x_0 v, x_0 v^2$,

where v is independent of x_0 and x_0 is one solution of the congruence.

2. If $p \equiv 2 \pmod 3$, show that $x^3 \equiv a \pmod p$ has exactly one solution. Express it in the form a^r, where r is a fixed integer independent of a.

3. Assuming Theorem 5.4, prove that $x^4 \equiv -1 \pmod p$ for an odd prime p, if and only if $p \equiv 1 \pmod 8$; that is, all odd prime divisors of $x^4 + 1$ are congruent to 1 $\pmod 8$. Why does this show that there are infinitely many primes congruent to 1 $\pmod 8$?

4. By the method of Exercise 3, prove that for any positive integer r there are infinitely many primes of the form

$$p = 1 + 2^{r+1} \cdot N, N = 1, 2, 3, \cdots.$$

There is a famous theorem of Dirichlet which generalized the above results. It states, in fact, that for any integers a and b without a common factor greater than 1 there are infinitely many primes of the form $a + Nb$, $N = 0, 1, 2, \cdots$. In other words, if $(a,b) = 1$ there are infinitely many primes in the arithmetic progression

$$a, a + b, a + 2b, a + 3b, \cdots.$$

5.5. Primitive roots

There is another question connected with power residues suggested by Fermat's Theorem. Certainly there are often smaller powers of a than a^{p-1} which are congruent to 1 $\pmod p$, for example, $2^3 \equiv 1 \pmod 7$, but for each prime p is there an integer a such that no power of a smaller than $p - 1$ is congruent to 1 $\pmod p$? For instance, the successive powers of 3 $\pmod 7$ are congruent to $3,2,6,4,5,1 \pmod 7$, and 3 is such a number. We call a number a, a **primitive root** $\pmod p$ or a primitive root of p if $p - 1$ is the least positive power of a which is congruent to 1 $\pmod p$ and prove

Theorem 5.5a. Every prime p has $\phi(p - 1)$ primitive roots, where ϕ is the Euler ϕ-function.

In fact, suppose we say that "a belongs to the exponent k $\pmod p$" if k is the least positive power of a which is congruent to 1 $\pmod p$ and see that Theorem 5.5a is included in

Theorem 5.5b. If k is any divisor of $p - 1$, there are $\phi(k)$ numbers (mod p) which belong to k (mod p).

Theorem 2.6b implies that k must be a divisor of $p - 1$. By Exercise 17 in Exercises 2.9, we have seen that if a belongs to k (mod p) then a^r also belongs to k (mod p) if and only if $(r, k) = 1$. Hence, for each divisor k of $p - 1$, there are $\phi(k)$ or no numbers belonging to k (mod p). If then we let $\rho(k)$ stand for the number of integers belonging to k (mod p), we see that for each k, $\rho(k)$ is either 0 or $\phi(k)$. Since every number from 1 to $p - 1$ belongs to some k (mod p), we have

$$p - 1 = \rho(1) + \rho(k_1) + \cdots + \rho(k_u),$$

where $1, k_2, k_3, \cdots, k_u$ are the divisors of $p - 1$. However we showed in Theorem 2.10b that

$$p - 1 = \phi(1) + \phi(k_1) + \cdots + \phi(k_u).$$

Hence $\rho(k_i) = \phi(k_i)$ for every k_i, and our theorem is proved.

For example, we have the following:

TABLE I

N	1	2	3	4	5	6	7	8	9	10	11	12
Belongs (mod 13) to	1	12	3	6	4	12	12	4	3	6	12	2

Note that $4 = \phi(12)$ numbers belong to 12; $2 = \phi(6)$ to 6; $2 = \phi(4)$ to 4; $2 = \phi(3)$ to 3; $1 = \phi(2)$ to 2; and $1 = \phi(1)$ to 1.

The primitive roots of a prime p serve a very useful purpose in that they can be made a basis for a kind of logarithm which expedites congruential computation. Notice that from the table above, 2 is a primitive root (mod 13). A table of the residues of the powers of 2 (mod 13) is below:

TABLE II

n	1	2	3	4	5	6	7	8	9	10	11	12
2^n	2	4	8	3	6	12	11	9	5	10	7	1

The values of n are usually called the **indices** for the numbers 2^n for the primitive root 2. We shall adopt the nomenclature of logarithms and write

$$\log_{g,p} a = b \text{ to mean } g^b \equiv a \pmod{p}$$

for g, a primitive root (mod p). For instance, we would have from Table II, $\log_{2,13} 5 = 9$. Any number except 0 (mod 13) will thus have a log to the base 2 (or any other primitive root). The following examples illustrate the use of a table of indices or logs.

EXAMPLE 1. Solve $3x \equiv 5$ (mod 13). Table II shows that $3 \equiv 2^4$, $5 \equiv 2^9$ (mod 13). Hence our congruence may be written $2^4 x \equiv 2^9$ (mod 13) and $x \equiv 2^{9-4} = 2^5 \equiv 6$ (mod 13). How would you similarly solve $5x \equiv 3$ (mod 13)?

EXAMPLE 2. Solve $x^4 \equiv 7$ (mod 13); that is, $x^4 \equiv 2^{11}$ (mod 13). If there were a solution, x would be a power of 2, say $x \equiv 2^r$, and then $x^4 \equiv 2^{4r}$ and $2^{4r} \equiv 2^{11}$ (mod 13), which would imply (why?) that $4r \equiv 11$ (mod 12), an impossibility, showing that there can be no solution. We could have deduced this from Theorem 5.4, since $12/4 = 3$ and $7^3 \not\equiv 1$ (mod 13).

EXAMPLE 3. Solve $x^5 \equiv 7$ (mod 13); that is, $x^5 \equiv 2^{11}$ (mod 13). Let $x = 2^r$ and see that we must have $5r \equiv 11$ (mod 12). The only solution of the last congruence is $r = 7$, and hence the only solution of our given congruence is $x = 2^7 \equiv 11$ (mod 13).

Exercises 5.5

1. Use Table II to find all solutions of $x^4 \equiv 9$ (mod 13).

2. What other primitive roots does 13 have beside 2? Form a table, such as Table II, for each such root. Use one table to solve the congruence in the previous exercise.

3. Show how Table I could be constructed from Table II.

4. Using primitive roots, prove Theorem 5.4.

5. Show that $x^e \equiv a$ (mod p) is solvable if and only if $\log_{g,p} a$ is divisible by $(e, p - 1)$ for every primitive root g.

6. How would you define a primitive root (mod p^k) where p is a prime? Using your definition, find whether 9 has a primitive root. Does 8 have a primitive root?

7. Find all the numbers that belong to $\phi(m)$ for $m = 3,9,27$.

8. Find all the numbers which belong to 2^{k-2} (mod 2^k) for $k = 3,4,5,6$.

5.6.   Primitive roots modulo powers of a prime

It is natural to call a a primitive root of p^k if $\phi(p^k)$ is the smallest power of a which is congruent to 1 (mod p). Exercise 6 above shows that 8 has no primitive root but the following theorem holds:

Theorem 5.6a. If p is an odd prime, p^r has a primitive root for every positive integer r.

First, we find primitive roots (mod p^2). Let a be a primitive root (mod p), and suppose $a + kp$ belongs to t (mod p^2). Now, $(a + kp)^t \equiv 1$ (mod p) implies $t \equiv 0$ (mod $p - 1$), and since from Theorems 2.6a and 2.6b, t also divides $p(p - 1) = \phi(p^2)$ it must be either $p - 1$ or $p(p - 1)$. If it is the former we have

$$(a + kp)^{p-1} \equiv 1 \pmod{p^2}; \text{ that is,}$$
$$(a + kp)^p \equiv a + kp \pmod{p^2}.$$

Thus $a^p - a \equiv kp$ (mod p^2), which holds if and only if $k \equiv (a^p - a)/p$ (mod p). Hence, for $p - 1$ values of k the last congruence fails to hold, and for these values $a + kp$ is a primitive root; that is, p^2 has $(p - 1)$ $\phi(p - 1)$ primitive roots, since there are $\phi(p - 1)$ primitive roots, a, of p. We shall show below that all primitive roots of p^2 are obtained in this manner.

Before we consider primitive roots of higher powers of p, notice that 2 is the only primitive root of 3. The primitive roots of 9 are 2 and 5 but not 8. However, all the numbers congruent to 2 (mod 9) are primitive roots of 27, and a similar statement may be made for numbers congruent to 5 (mod 9). This suggests that *any* primitive root (mod p^2) may be a primitive root for all higher powers of p. We now show that this is the case.

First, we need the following auxiliary result:

Lemma: Let p be an odd prime and $a^t \equiv 1 + kp^s$ (mod p^{s+1}) with $s \geq 1$; then

$$a^{tp^r} \equiv 1 + kp^{s+r} \pmod{p^{s+r+1}}.$$

First, we prove the lemma for $r = 1$. The congruence of the hypothesis is equivalent to the equation

$$a^t = 1 + kp^s + up^{s+1},$$

where u is an integer. Raise both sides of the equation to the pth power and obtain

$$a^t = (1 + kp^s + up^{s+1})^p = 1 + p(kp^s + up^{s+1}) +$$
$$(p/2)(p - 1)(kp^s + up^{s+1})^2 + \cdots$$
$$\equiv 1 + kp^{s+1} \pmod{p^{s+2}},$$

since all terms but the first two in the expansion are divisible by p^{s+2}. This completes the proof for $r = 1$.

To prove the lemma by induction assume it true for r replaced by $r - 1$; that is, assume that the hypothesis of the lemma implies

$$a^{tp^{r-1}} \equiv 1 + kp^{s+r-1} \pmod{p^{s+r}}.$$

If, in the hypothesis of the lemma, we replace t by tp^{r-1} and s by $s + r - 1$, we have the last congruence. Hence, by the conclusion of the lemma for $r = 1$, it follows that

$$(a^{tp^{r-1}})^p \equiv 1 + kp^{s+r-1+1} \pmod{p^{s+r+1}},$$

which is what we wished to prove.

Second, every primitive root of p^{r+s} is a primitive root of p^s, for if a belongs to $t \pmod{p^s}$ we have $a^t = 1 + kp^s$ and hence, by the lemma, $a^{tp^r} \equiv 1 \pmod{p^{s+r}}$; and if a is a primitive root of p^{s+r}, $tp^r \equiv 0 \pmod{\phi(p^{s+r})}$. However, $\phi(p^{s+r}) = p^r\phi(p^s)$, and hence $t \equiv 0 \pmod{\phi(p^s)}$, and a is a primitive root of p^s.

Third, suppose a is a primitive root of p^2. From what we have just proved it must be a primitive root $\pmod p$, and hence $a^{p-1} = 1 + kp$, where k is prime to p. Then, by the lemma with $t = p - 1$ and $s = 1$, we have

(1) $$a^{\phi(p^{r+1})} \equiv 1 + kp^{r+1} \pmod{p^{r+2}}.$$

Thus, if $r = 1$, $a^{\phi(p^2)} \equiv 1 + kp^2 \pmod{p^3}$, which shows that $a^{\phi(p^2)} \not\equiv 1 \pmod{p^3}$. If, however, a belongs to $t \pmod{p^3}$, $a^t \equiv 1 \pmod{p^2}$ implies t is divisible by $\phi(p^2)$, and hence t must be $\phi(p^2)$ or $\phi(p^3)$. The former would contradict the previous incongruence. Hence t must be $\phi(p^3)$, and a is a primitive root of p^3. Similarly, (1) implies $a^{\phi(p^2)} \not\equiv 1 \pmod{p^4}$, and thus a is a primitive root of p^4. Continuing in this fashion, we see that every primitive root of p^2 is a primitive root of p^r for all r, and every odd prime p.

The number 2 seems to be a peculiar prime. For instance, the Euler phi-function of a power of p is a power of p only when $p = 2$. One other respect in which it differs in behavior from the other primes is that no power of 2 beyond 4 has a primitive root. Notice that 3 belongs to 2 (mod 8), 4 (mod 16), 8 (mod 32), and so on. In fact, we have

Theorem 5.6b. If $t > 3$, an odd number $1 + 2n$ belongs to 2^{t-2} (mod 2^t) or a lesser power of 2 according as $n \equiv 1,2$ (mod 4) or 0,3 (mod 4).

This depends on the following auxiliary result, which we prove first.

Lemma: If $t > 3$, then

$$(1 + 2n)^{2^{t-3}} \equiv 1 + 2^{t-2}(n - n^2 + 2n^4) \pmod{2^t}.$$

This lemma can be shown by expanding the left side by the binomial theorem, but this leads to certain complications which may be avoided if we elect to prove it by induction as follows.

If $t = 4$, $(1 + 2n)^2 = 1 + 4n + 4n^2 = 1 + 4(n + n^2)$, which gives the formula of the lemma, since $n + n^2 \equiv n - n^2 + 2n^4 \pmod 4$ for all n. If $t = 5$, $(1 + 2n)^4 = 1 + 4 \cdot 2n + 6 \cdot 4n^2 + 4 \cdot 8n^3 + 16n^4$

$$\equiv 1 + 8(n + 3n^2 + 2n^4) \pmod{32}$$
$$\equiv 1 + 8(n - n^2 + 2n^4) \pmod{32}.$$

We now assume the lemma for $t \geq 5$ and seek to prove it for $t + 1$. That is, we may assume

$$(1 + 2n)^{2^{t-3}} = 1 + 2^{t-2}(n - n^2 + 2n^4) + 2^t r,$$

where r is an integer. Squaring both sides, we get

$$(1 + 2n)^{2^{t-2}} \equiv 1 + 2^{t-1}(n - n^2 + 2n^4) \pmod{2^{t+1}},$$

since $2(t - 2) \geq t + 1$ when $t \geq 5$. This completes the induction and proves the lemma.

To prove the theorem, notice that if $n \equiv 0$ or 3 (mod 4), $n - n^2 + 2n^4 \equiv 0$ (mod 4) and hence $(1 + 2n)^{2^{t-3}} \equiv 1$ (mod 2^t) and $1 + 2n$ belongs to a power less than 2^{t-2} (mod 2^t). On the other hand, if $n \equiv 1$ or 2 (mod 4), $n - n^2 + 2n^4 \equiv 2$ (mod 4) and $(1 + 2n)^{2^{t-3}} \equiv 1 + 2^{t-1} \not\equiv 1$ (mod 2^t). However, $(1 + 2n)^{2^{t-2}} \equiv 1$ (mod 2^t). Hence we have

Corollary 5.6b. If $t \geq 4$, m belongs to 2^{t-2} (mod 2^t) if and only if $m \equiv \pm 3$ (mod 8); otherwise m belongs to a smaller power. If $t = 3$, the numbers 3,5, and 7 all belong to 2 (mod 8).

Theorem 5.6c. If we define a primitive root (mod m) to be a number a such that $\phi(m)$ is the least power of a which is congruent to 1 (mod m), then m has a primitive root if and only if m is one of the numbers

$$2, 4, p^r, 2p^r,$$

where p is an odd prime. We leave the proof as an exercise.

Exercises 5.6

1. Are there values of s and r such that $5^r \equiv 3^s$ (mod 2^6), where $0 < r \leq 2^4$ and $0 < s \leq 2^4$?

2. Since Corollary 5.6b shows that 5 belongs to 2^{t-2} (mod 2^t), why does it follow that 5^r takes on exactly 2^{t-2} different values (mod 2^t) as r ranges over the positive integers not greater than 2^{t-2}? Hence show that for every odd number a there is a positive integer r such that, for the proper choice of sign

$$a \equiv \pm 5^r \;(\text{mod } 2^t),\; 0 < r \leq 2^{t-2}.$$

Also show that r (with these restrictions) and the sign are unique. Would the same be true if 5 were replaced by 3?

3. Suppose $m = 2^{t_0}p_1^{t_1}p_2^{t_2}\cdots p_s^{t_s}$, where the p_i are distinct odd primes. Let g_0 be chosen so that

$$g_0 \equiv 5 \;(\text{mod } 8),\; g_0 \equiv 1 \;(\text{mod } m/2^{t_0}),$$

the ambiguous sign $\pm$ so that

$$a \equiv \pm 1 \;(\text{mod } 4),$$

and, for each positive i, choose g_i a primitive root (mod $p_i^{t_i}$) such that

$$g_i \equiv 1 \;(\text{mod } m/p_i^{t_i}).$$

Why is such a choice possible? Show that for every integer a, prime to m, there are positive integers $r_i \leq \phi(p_i^{t_i})$ and an integer r_0 which is zero or not greater than $t_0 - 2$, such that

$$a \equiv \pm g_0^{r_0}g_1^{r_1}g_2^{r_2}\cdots g_s^{r_s} \;(\text{mod } m),$$

for the above choice of ambiguous sign. HINT: Show that the last congruence holds for each prime power dividing m. Furthermore, show that the g_i and a uniquely determine the r_i and, if m is divisible by 4, the ambiguous sign.

4. Show that if m is factored as in Exercise 3 and a is any number prime to m then $a^k \equiv 1 \pmod{m}$ where k is the least common multiple of

$$2^{t_0 - 2}, \ \phi(p_1^{t_1}), \ \cdots, \ \phi(p_s^{t_s}).$$

Is there a number a such that this k is the least power congruent to 1 $\pmod{m}$? Under what conditions is $k = \phi(m)$?

5. Prove Theorem 5.6c.

6. Find the number of primitive roots of p^r, for p an odd prime.

7. How many numbers will there be belonging to $2^{t-2} \pmod{2^t}$?

· 6 ·

Quadratic Residues

6.1. Summary of previous results

Recall that we have called a a quadratic residue (mod m) if $(a,m) = 1$ and

$$x^2 \equiv a \pmod{m}$$

has a solution (see Exercises 5.3). If $(a,m) = 1$ and the congruence is not solvable, we call a a quadratic nonresidue or, simply, nonresidue. If $(a,m) \neq 1$, a is neither a quadratic residue nor a nonresidue.

In the same exercises we showed that each odd prime number p has $(p-1)/2$ quadratic residues and the same number of nonresidues. This could also be seen from the fact that the even powers of a primitive root of p are quadratic residues and the odd powers are the nonresidues. Why?

Furthermore, an immediate consequence of Theorem 5.4 is

Theorem 6.1. (Euler's Criterion.) If $(a,p) = 1$ and p is an odd prime, then a is a quadratic residue (mod p) if

$$a^{(p-1)/2} \equiv +1 \pmod{p},$$

and a nonresidue if

$$a^{(p-1)/2} \equiv -1 \pmod{p}.$$

One of these congruences must hold if $(a, p) = 1$.

Corollary 6.1. If $p \equiv 1 \pmod 4$, then -1 is a quadratic residue of p; if $p \equiv -1 \pmod 4$, it is a nonresidue.

The proof of the theorem and corollary is left as an exercise.

Exercises 6.1

1. Show why Theorem 6.1 follows from Theorem 5.4, and why the corollary follows from the theorem.

2. Show that the even powers of a primitive root of p are quadratic residues (mod p) and the odd powers nonresidues.

3. Show that the statement in Exercise 2 remains true if p is replaced by p^r, where now p is an odd prime.

4. If a is prime to p, why must one of the congruences of Theorem 6.1 hold?

5. Show that b is a quadratic residue of an odd prime p if and only if it is a quadratic residue of all powers of p. There are at least two methods of proof, suggested as follows:

   a. Use Exercise 3, above, and the fact that any primitive root of p^r is a primitive root of p.
   b. Show that if x_0 is a root of $x^2 \equiv a$ (mod p), then k may be determined so that $(x_0 + kp)^2 \equiv a$ (mod p^2), and so on for higher powers of p.

6. Show that b is a quadratic residue of 2^t, $t \geq 3$ if and only if $b \equiv 1$ (mod 8). Two methods of proof are

   a. Show that the even powers of 5 (mod 2^t) are congruent to the numbers congruent to 1 (mod 8) and less than 2^t, in other words, that $b \equiv 1$ (mod 8) implies $5^{2x} \equiv b$ (mod 2^t) is solvable for x.
   b. Show that if x_0 is a root of $x^2 \equiv a$ (mod 8) then k may be determined so that $(x_0 + 4k)^2 \equiv a$ (mod 16), and so on for higher powers of 2.

6.2. The Legendre Symbol

The results of Exercises 5 and 6, above, show that whether or not a number is a quadratic residue of a power of a prime depends on the same information for the prime itself. For purposes of easy reference we list these results as

Theorem 6.2a. A number a is a quadratic residue of p^r if and only if

   1. It is a quadratic residue of p for p odd,
   2. $a \equiv 1$ (mod 8) if $p = 2$, $r \geqq 3$,
   3. $a \equiv 1$ (mod 2^r) if $p = 2$ and $r = 1$ or 2.

The Chinese Remainder Theorem shows that the quadratic residues of a composite number may be found from the quadratic residues of its prime power factors. We leave as an exercise the proof of

Theorem 6.2b. The number b is a quadratic residue of a composite number m prime to b if and only if it is a quadratic residue of each odd prime factor of m and, in addition,

$$b \equiv 1 \pmod 4 \text{ if } m \equiv 0 \pmod 4,$$
$$b \equiv 1 \pmod 8 \text{ if } m \equiv 0 \pmod 8.$$

Though Euler's Criterion gives a way of determining the **quadratic character** of a number (mod p), that is, whether or not it is a quadratic residue, it is cumbersome in practice. There is a much more elegant method embodied in the Quadratic Reciprocity Law which we shall prove later in this chapter. The first step on the road to this result is the Legendre Symbol $(a|p)$, defined for p an odd prime as follows:

$$(a|p) = 1 \text{ if } a \text{ is a quadratic residue of } p,$$
$$(a|p) = -1 \text{ if } a \text{ is a quadratic nonresidue of } p,$$
$$(a|p) = 0 \text{ if } a \equiv 0 \pmod p.$$

This symbol was originally written $\left(\dfrac{a}{p}\right)$, but the notation given above is coming into vogue and is much more popular with the printers. There is a certain elegance about this symbol, since it has the properties listed below.

Theorem 6.2c. The Legendre Symbol has the following properties:

1. If $(a, p) = 1$, $(a|p) \equiv a^{(p-1)/2} \pmod p$ by Euler's Criterion.
2. The symbol is multiplicative, that is,

$$(a|p)(b|p) = (ab|p).$$

3. If $a \equiv b \pmod p$, then $(a|p) = (b|p)$.
4. If $(r, p) = 1$, then $(ar^2|p) = (a|p)$. In words, a square factor prime to p may be deleted from the left portion of any symbol without altering its value.

The proof is left as an exercise.

The Legendre Symbol is a particular example of what is called a **character,** which could be defined as follows: Let g be a primitive root of

p, and let ρ be a number for which $\rho^{p-1} = 1$; that is, ρ is a $p - 1$ root of unity. Then define the symbol

$$(a|p)_\rho$$

to be zero if $(a,p) \neq 1$, and ρ^t if $(a,p) = 1$, where $t = \log_{g,p} a$. You must recall that $t = \log_{g,p} a$ was defined to be that unique positive integer less than p for which $a \equiv g^t \pmod{p}$. For the Legendre Symbol, ρ is -1, and the value of the character is independent of g. Usually the value of the character depends not only on ρ but on g.

Exercises 6.2

1. Prove Theorem 6.2b.

2. If $p \equiv 1 \pmod 3$ and $\rho = w$, an imaginary cube root of unity, show that the character $(a|p)_w$ is not independent of the primitive root of p but that if $(a|p)_w = 1$ for one primitive root it is equal to 1 for every primitive root.

3. Prove Theorem 6.2c.

4. Prove that properties 2 and 3 of Theorem 6.2c hold for the symbol $(a|p)_\rho$.

5. Prove that $(1|p) + (2|p) + \cdots + (p - 1|p) = 0$, if p is a prime. The same result may be shown to hold for the character defined above.

6.3.   Gauss's Lemma

There is a lemma of Gauss which gives a rather curious way of finding the quadratic character of a number (mod p). From a computational point of view it is not very useful, but it has at least two claims to importance: First, it gives a means of determining the primes of which 2 is a quadratic residue; and second, it is an important step on the road to the Quadratic Reciprocity Law whose proof is the goal of this chapter.

Before stating the lemma formally, let us see how it works in a particular example. Suppose we wish to determine whether or not 7 is a quadratic residue of 17. Write

$$1 \cdot 7, \; 2 \cdot 7, \; 3 \cdot 7, \; 4 \cdot 7, \; 5 \cdot 7, \; 6 \cdot 7, \; 7 \cdot 7, \; 8 \cdot 7,$$

that is, the first $(p-1)/2$ multiples of 7, where $p = 17$. Their least positive residues (mod 17) are in order

$$7, 14, 4, 11, 1, 8, 15, 5.$$

Notice that each residue is derived from its predecessor by adding 7 and, if necessary, reducing (mod 17). Now, three of these are greater than $17/2$, and Gauss's Lemma affirms that $(7|17) = (-1)^3 = -1$; that is, 7 is a nonresidue of 17. In a similar fashion, 13 can be shown to be a quadratic residue of 17.

Theorem 6.3a. (Gauss's Lemma.) If p is an odd prime, $(q,p) = 1$, and u is the number of least positive residues of the set

(1) $$q, 2q, 3q, \cdots, q(p-1)/2$$

which are greater than $p/2$, then

$$(q|p) = (-1)^u.$$

Let $b_1, b_2, \cdots, b_t$ be those least positive residues (mod p) of the set (1) which are less than $p/2$ and $c_1, c_2, \cdots, c_u$ those which are greater than $p/2$. Then $u + t = (p-1)/2$, and the numbers

(2) $$b_1, b_2, \cdots, b_t, p - c_1, p - c_2, \cdots, p - c_u$$

are all positive and less than $p/2$.

If we could show that the numbers of (2) were all distinct (mod p), they would have to be $1, 2, \cdots, (p-1)/2$ in some order, and we would have

$$q(2q)(3q) \cdots q(p-1)/2 \equiv b_1 b_2 \cdots b_t c_1 c_2 \cdots c_u$$
$$\equiv (-1)^u b_1 b_2 \cdots b_t (p - c_1)(p - c_2) \cdots (p - c_u)$$
$$\equiv (-1)^u \left(\frac{p-1}{2}\right)! \pmod{p}.$$

That is,

$$q^{(p-1)/2}\left(\frac{p-1}{2}\right)! \equiv (-1)^u \left(\frac{p-1}{2}\right)! \pmod{p}.$$

Since $\left(\frac{p-1}{2}\right)!$ is prime to p, we may divide both sides of the congruence by it and have

$$q^{(p-1)/2} \equiv (-1)^u \pmod{p}.$$

Use of Euler's Criterion then would complete the proof.

It remains to show that the numbers of (2) are distinct (mod p). Suppose $b_i \equiv b_j \pmod{p}$, with $i \neq j$. Then $b_i \equiv rq$, $b_j \equiv sq \pmod{p}$ with $r \neq s$ would imply $rq \equiv sq \pmod{p}$, and hence $r \equiv s \pmod{p}$. This is impossible, since r and s are positive, distinct, and less than $p/2$. Similarly, $p - c_i \not\equiv p - c_j \pmod{p}$. Finally, if $b_i \equiv p - c_j$, where $b_i \equiv rq$, $c_j \equiv sq \pmod{p}$, we would have $rq \equiv -sq \pmod{p}$; that is, $r \equiv -s \pmod{p}$, or $r + s \equiv 0 \pmod{p}$. This is impossible, since both r and s are positive and less than $p/2$. Thus the proof of the theorem is complete.

The first use we make of this theorem is to show

Theorem 6.3b. If p is an odd prime,

$$(2|p) = (-1)^{(p^2-1)/8};$$

that is, $(2|p) = 1$ if $p \equiv \pm 1 \pmod{8}$, and $(2|p) = -1$ if $p \equiv \pm 3 \pmod{8}$.

To show this, let $q = 2$ in Theorem 6.3a, and the set (1) becomes

$$(3) \qquad\qquad 2, \, 2 \cdot 2, \, 3 \cdot 2, \, \cdots, \, 2(p-1)/2.$$

These numbers are all less than p and hence are all least positive residues (mod p). Hence we must determine how many are greater than $p/2$. First, if $p \equiv 1 \pmod{4}$, then

$$2(p-1)/4 < p/2 \text{ and } 2 \cdot (p+3)/4 > p/2.$$

Hence $u = (p-1)/2 - (p-1)/4 = (p-1)/4$; thus u is even if $p \equiv 1 \pmod{8}$, and odd if $p \equiv -3 \pmod{8}$. Second, if $p \equiv -1 \pmod{4}$, then

$$2(p-3)/4 < p/2 \text{ and } 2(p+1)/4 > p/2.$$

Hence $u = (p-1)/2 - (p-3)/4 = (p+1)/4$; thus u is even if $p \equiv -1 \pmod{8}$, and odd if $p \equiv 3 \pmod{8}$. Hence u is even if $p \equiv \pm 1 \pmod{8}$, and odd if $p \equiv \pm 3 \pmod{8}$. In the former case $(p^2 - 1)/8$ is even, and in the latter it is odd. This proves the theorem. (For other proofs of this theorem, see Ref. 14, pp. 278 ff.)

There is another criterion for quadratic character which takes us further along the way to our ultimate goal. It is

Theorem 6.3c. If

$$M = [q/p] + [2q/p] + \cdots + [(p-1)q/2p],$$

that is, if M is the sum of the greatest integers in the numbers of set (1) of Theorem 6.3a, divided by p, then

$$u \equiv M + (p^2 - 1)(q - 1)/8 \pmod 2,$$

where u is defined in Theorem 6.3a, and p is an odd prime. Recall $(q|p) = (-1)^u$.

First notice that

$$iq = p \cdot [iq/p] + r_i,$$

where r_i is the least positive residue of $iq \pmod p$ and hence is one of the b_i's or c_i's of Theorem 6.3a. Thus

$$
\begin{aligned}
\sum_{i=1}^{(p-1)/2} iq &= pM + r_1 + r_2 + \cdots + r_{t+u} \\
&= pM + b_1 + b_2 + \cdots + b_t + c_1 + c_2 + \cdots + c_u \\
&= pM + b_1 + \cdots + b_t + up - (p - c_1) - (p - c_2) - \cdots \\
&\quad - (p - c_u) \\
&\equiv pM + up + \sum_{i=1}^{t} b_i + \sum_{i=1}^{u}(p - c_i) \pmod 2.
\end{aligned}
$$

Then, since the numbers of (2) are $1, 2, \cdots, (p - 1)/2$ in some order and p is odd,

$$
\begin{aligned}
\sum iq &\equiv M + u + \sum i \pmod 2, \\
u &\equiv M + \sum i - q \cdot \sum i \pmod 2,
\end{aligned}
$$

all sums being over i from 1 to $(p - 1)/2$. Each of the sums in the last congruence is, by the formula for the sum of an arithmetic progression, equal to $(p^2 - 1)/8$. Hence

$$u \equiv M + (1 - q)(p^2 - 1)/8 \pmod 2,$$

and the theorem is proved, since $1 - q \equiv q - 1 \pmod 2$.

Exercises 6.3

1. Show that Theorem 6.3c implies Theorem 6.3b. Show that $(m^2 - 1)/8$ is even if and only if $m \equiv \pm 1 \pmod 8$.

2. Of what primes is -2 a quadratic residue?

3. Use Theorem 6.3c to find the quadratic character of 13 with respect to 17.

4. Show that if $q = 3$ in Theorem 6.3c then $M = (p - 1)/6$ or $(p + 1)/6$ according as $p \equiv 1 \pmod 3$ or $p \equiv -1 \pmod 3$, hence that

$$u \equiv (p - 1)(3p + 5)/12 \text{ or } (p + 1)(3p - 1)/12 \pmod 2$$

in the respective cases. This shows that 3 is a quadratic residue of an odd prime p if and only if

$$p \equiv 1 \text{ or } 11 \pmod{12}.$$

5. Of what primes is -3 a quadratic residue?

6. We showed in Exercise 3 of Exercises 5.4 that there are infinitely many primes of the form $8N + 1$. If $x^2 - 2$ is divisible by an odd prime, the prime must be congruent to $\pm 1 \pmod 8$, since 2 is a quadratic residue of only these primes; not all the prime factors of $x^2 - 2$ can be $\equiv 1 \pmod 8$, since for x odd, $x^2 - 2 \equiv -1 \pmod 8$. Hence, for each odd x, $x^2 - 2$ has a prime factor $p \equiv -1 \pmod 8$. Why does this imply that there are infinitely many primes of the form $8N - 1$? Devise similar proofs for the forms $8N + 3$, $8N + 5$.

7. Of what primes is 6 a quadratic residue?

6.4. The Quadratic Reciprocity Law

This law has been characterized as one of the most beautiful results in the theory of numbers. It was stated by Euler in 1783 and first proved by Gauss thirteen years later, who gave several proofs. There have since been many proofs. Because the elegance of the result is not at first apparent, after stating it we shall first show how it is used.

Theorem 6.4a. (The Quadratic Reciprocity Law.) If p and q are two distinct odd primes, then

$$(q|p)(p|q) = (-1)^t,$$

where $t = (p - 1)(q - 1)/4$. That is,

$$(q|p) = (p|q) \text{ if } p \equiv 1 \pmod 4 \text{ or } q \equiv 1 \pmod 4,$$
$$(q|p) = -(p|q) \text{ if } p \equiv q \equiv 3 \pmod 4.$$

The second form of the law, which is easier to use in practice, follows from the first, since t is even unless both p and q are congruent to

3 (mod 4). First, let us see how the law applies to the evaluation of (35|71). By property 2 of the Legendre Symbol this is equal to (5|71) (7|71). The Quadratic Reciprocity Law and property 3 of the Legendre Symbol gives the following:

$$(5|71) = (71|5) = (1|5) = 1,$$
$$(7|71) = -(71|7) = -(1|7) = -1,$$

and the product of the two values shows that 35 is a nonresidue of 71. We shall later remove some of the restrictions on p and q with the result that computation can be shortened to $(35|71) = -(71|35) = -(1|35) = -1$, but we first shall prove our result when both numbers in the symbol are primes.

To prove the law, notice that q odd implies from Theorem 6.3c that $u \equiv M \pmod 2$ and hence

$$(q|p) = (-1)^M.$$

Thus, if N is that sum obtained from M by interchanging p and q, we have

$$(q|p)(p|q) = (-1)^{M+N}.$$

Hence it remains to prove that

(4) $$M + N = (p-1)(q-1)/4.$$

We shall use Eisenstein's geometric proof, which is as follows: On a rectangular coordinate system, let the line L connect the origin with the point (p, q). Let R denote the region bounded by the lines $x = p/2$, $y = q/2$ and the x and y axes, not including any of the bounding lines. (See the illustration for $p = 11$, $q = 5$.)

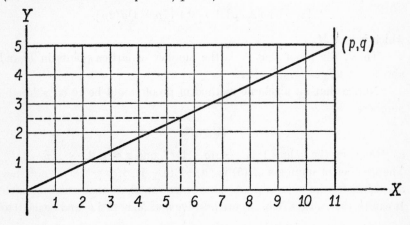

The proof consists in counting in two ways the **lattice points** (that is, the points with integral coordinates) within the region R.

The simplest way to count them is to notice that the lattice points form a rectangle whose horizontal dimension is $(p-1)/2$ and whose vertical dimension is $(q-1)/2$. Hence R contains in its interior

$$\frac{p-1}{2} \cdot \frac{q-1}{2}$$

lattice points. We then shall establish (4) by showing that in R there are

1. No lattice points on L,
2. M lattice points below L,
3. N lattice points above L.

Hence it will follow that there are $M + N$ lattice points in R and $M + N = (p-1)(q-1)/4$.

First, since the equation of L is $py = qx$ and p and q are relatively prime, p must divide the x-coordinate of any lattice point on L, and q must divide the y-coordinate. Hence there is no lattice point on L closer to the origin than the point (q,p). This point is outside R. Therefore L contains no lattice points within R.

Second, on the line $x = 1$ the y coordinates of the lattice points below L in R are $1, 2, \cdots, [q/p]$; that is, there are $[q/p]$ lattice points in R, below L and on $x = 1$. Similarly, there are $[2q/p]$ lattice points in R, below L and on $x = 2$. Hence the total number of lattice points in R and below L is

$$[q/p] + [2q/p] + \cdots + [(p-1)q/2p],$$

which is just M.

Third, the proof that N is the number of lattice points in R and above L is left as an exercise.

Notice that an algebraic method of proof would be to consider the numbers

(5) $py - qx,$

as y takes on the values $1, 2, \cdots, (q-1)/2$, and $x = 1, 2, \cdots, (p-1)/2$. The number of numbers of (5) is $(p-1)(q-1)/4$ (whether or not they are distinct is immaterial). As above, we can show that none are zero. It can be shown that N of (5) are positive and M negative and hence that

(4) holds.   The connection with the geometric argument may be seen, since the line L is $py - qx = 0$, and if (x, y) is any point above L, $y > qx/p$, that is, $py - qx > 0$ and, for points below L, $py - qx < 0$.

EXAMPLE 1.   Find $(71|73)$.   Now $(71|73) = (73|71)$ since $73 \equiv 1$ (mod 4) and $(73|71) = (2|71)$ by property 3 of the Legendre Symbol. Finally, $(2|71) = 1$ by Theorem 6.3b, since $71 \equiv 7$ (mod 8).   Hence $(71|73) = 1$, and 71 is a quadratic residue of 73.   One could also evaluate the symbol as follows: $(71|73) = (-2|73) = (-1|73)(2|73) = 1 \cdot 1 = 1$, by properties 3 and 2 of the Legendre Symbol, Corollary 6.1, and Theorem 6.3b.

EXAMPLE 2.   Find $(55|73)$.   Here $(55|73) = (-18|73) = (-2|73)$ by properties 3 and 4 of the Legendre Symbol.   We have just shown $(-2|73)$ to be 1 and hence $(55|73) = 1$.

EXAMPLE 3.   Find $(186|301)$.   Now $(186|301) = (2|301)(3|301)$ $(31|301)$.

$(2|301)$ $= -1$, since $301 \equiv 5$ (mod 8),

$(3|301)$ $= (301|3) = (1|3) = 1$,

$(31|301)$ $= (301|31) = (22|31) = (-9|31) = (-1|31) = -1$.

Hence $(186|301) = 1$, and 186 is a quadratic residue of 301.

Exercises 6.4

1. Compute the following quadratic characters:

$$(17|89), \ (73|89), \ (10|137), \ (29|101).$$

2. Use the Quadratic Reciprocity Law to do Exercises 4 and 5 of the previous section.

3. Is 7 a quadratic residue of 65?   Is 14 a quadratic residue of 65?

4. In the proof of (4) show that N is the number of lattice points in R and above L.

5. Complete the algebraic proof of (4).

6.5. The Jacobi Symbol

There is an extension of the Legendre Symbol which shortens the computation. The Jacobi Symbol is defined as follows for odd numbers $P = p_1 p_2 \cdots p_k$, where the p's are primes not necessarily distinct:

$$(m|P) = (m|p_1)(m|p_2) \cdots (m|p_k).$$

First, it should be noted that $(m|P) = 1$ *does not* imply that m is a quadratic residue of P. For instance, $(7|65) = (7|5)(7|13) = 1$, since $(7|5) = (7|13) = -1$. But the latter shows that 7 is not a quadratic residue of 5 and hence cannot be one of 65, since $x^2 \equiv 7 \pmod{65}$ solvable would imply $x^2 \equiv 7 \pmod 5$ solvable. For m to be a quadratic residue of P it must be one of *each factor of* P. However, if $(m|P) = -1$, one of the symbols $(m|p_1)$ must be -1, and hence m is a nonresidue of P. Thus $(m|P) = -1$ implies that m is a nonresidue of P, but if $(m|P) = 1$, then m is necessarily a quadratic residue of P *only if P is an odd prime.*

The usefulness of the Jacobi Symbol depends on its having the six properties of manipulation of the Legendre Symbol, which we list in

Theorem 6.5. The Jacobi Symbol $(a|P)$ for odd positive integers P has the following properties:

1. $(a|P)(b|P) = (ab|P)$.
2. If $a \equiv b \pmod P$, $(a|P) = (b|P)$.
3. If $(r,P) = 1$, $(ar^2|P) = (a|P)$.
4. $(-1|P) = (-1)^{(P-1)/2}$.
5. $(2|P) = (-1)^{(P^2-1)/8}$.
6. $(P|Q)(Q|P) = (-1)^t$, where $t = (P-1)(Q-1)/4$.

The proofs of the first three properties are left as exercises.
To prove Property 4, see that

$$(-1|P) = (-1|p_1)(-1|p_2) \cdots (-1|p_k) = (-1)^r, \quad r = \sum_{i=1}^{k} (p_i - 1)/2.$$

We have to show that r is of the same parity as $(P-1)/2$. However,

$$(P-1)/2 = (-1 + p_1 p_2 \cdots p_k)/2 = \left(-1 + \prod_{i=1}^{k} p_i\right),$$

where $\prod_{i=1}^{k} p_i$ is the abbreviated notation for the product of the p's, analogous to the Σ notation for their sum. Now,

$$\prod_{i=1}^{k} p_i = \prod_{i=1}^{k} (p_i - 1 + 1) \equiv 1 + \sum_{i=1}^{k} (p_i - 1) \pmod 4,$$

since any product of $p_i - 1$ and $p_j - 1$ is divisible by 4. Hence

$$(-1 + \mathop{\pi}_{i=1}^{k} p_i)/2 \equiv \sum_{i=1}^{k} (p_i - 1)/2 \pmod{2},$$

and property 4 is proved.

Property 5 is proved similarly, and this we leave as an exercise.

To prove Property 6, notice that

$$(P|Q) = \pi \ (p_i|q_j),$$

the product being over all prime factors p_i of P and prime factors q_j of Q, each repeated as often as it occurs in P or Q. Hence

$$(P|Q)(Q|P) = \mathop{\pi}_{i,j} \ (p_i|q_j)(q_j|p_i) = (-1)^t,$$

where

$$t = \sum \left(\frac{p_i - 1}{2}\right) \cdot \left(\frac{q_j - 1}{2}\right) \equiv \left(\sum \frac{p_i - 1}{2}\right)\left(\sum \frac{q_j - 1}{2}\right) \pmod{2}.$$

But we have just shown above that the first sum on the right is congruent to $(P - 1)/2 \pmod{2}$ and the second sum to $(Q - 1)/2 \pmod{2}$. Hence

$$(P|Q)(Q|P) \equiv t \equiv (P - 1)(Q - 1)/4 \pmod{2},$$

and property 6 holds.

Two examples will show the advantages of the Jacobi Symbol.

EXAMPLE 1. Is 85 a quadratic residue of 97? Using the Legendre Symbol would require evaluating $(5|97)$ and $(17|97)$; each would be seen to have the value -1, and hence their product is 1. Using the Jacobi Symbol, we have

$$(85|97) = (97|85) = (12|85) = (3|85) = (85|3) = (1|3) = 1.$$

Notice that we have shown that $(85|97) = 1$ and hence that 85 is a quadratic residue of 97, since the latter is a prime. On the other hand, $(12|85) = 1$ does not imply that 12 is a quadratic residue of 85. In fact, 12 is a nonresidue, since $(12|5) = -1$.

EXAMPLE 2. Find $(171|173)$. It is equal to $(173|171) = (2|171) = -1$.

Exercises 6.5

1. Use the Jacobi Symbol to compute the quadratic character of a with respect to m for the following pairs of values:

a	51	93	535	781	1303
m	103*	461*	877*	2305	2631

The values of m with asterisks are primes.

2. Prove Properties 1, 2, 3, and 5 of Theorem 6.5.

3. Define an extension of the Jacobi Symbol as follows: If a is positive, define $(a|-P)$ to be equal to $(a|P)$. Show that this symbol has the properties listed in Theorem 6.5, provided that in no symbol are both quantities negative. Why is this restriction necessary?

4. Use the results of Exercise 3 to find the primes of which -3 is a quadratic residue.

5. Find the conditions that the congruence

$$ax^2 + bx + c \equiv 0 \pmod{p}$$

be solvable.

6. Show that $x^2 \equiv a \pmod{p^t}$ is solvable for all primes p and all integers t if and only if a is the square of an integer.

7. Show that $x^2 \equiv a \pmod{m}$ is solvable for $(a,m) = 1$ if and only if $a = b^2c$, where c has no square factors and is a quadratic residue of m.

8. If P is an odd number, show that Property 1 of the Jacobi Symbol implies that

$$(m|P) \sum (i|P) = \sum (i|P),$$

where m is any integer prime to P and the sum is over all positive values of i less than P. Hence show that if m can be chosen so that $(m|P) \neq 1$ (when may this be done?) it follows that

$$\sum (i|P) = 0.$$

Does this mean that any composite number P has just as many quadratic residues as nonresidues?

9. Using the method suggested in the previous exercise, show that if $(a|p)_\rho$ is defined as in Section 2 and is not 1 for all a, then

$$\sum (i|p) = 0,$$

where the sum is over all positive i less than p.

10. Find all the values less than 40 taken on by the expression

$$x^2 + y^2$$

for x and y positive integers. Record how many times each value occurs, and guess what numbers in general are represented by this expression.

6.6. Sums of two squares

In this section we find what numbers are the sums of two squares, that is, for what integers m, the equation

(1) $$x^2 + y^2 = m$$

is solvable in integers x and y. The question may be reduced to consideration of m, a prime, by the following:

Lemma 6.6a. If m and n are each sums of two squares, so is $m \cdot n$.

To prove this, let $a^2 + b^2 = m$, $c^2 + d^2 = n$. Then $m \cdot n = (a^2 + b^2) \cdot (c^2 + d^2) = (ac + bd)^2 + (ad - bc)^2$.

The following is also useful:

Lemma 6.6b. If p is an odd prime dividing m in (1), then

$$x \equiv y \equiv 0 \pmod{p} \text{ or } p \equiv 1 \pmod 4.$$

Suppose $p \equiv 3 \pmod 4$ and $x^2 + y^2 \equiv 0 \pmod p$, with y prime to p. Then $y'y \equiv 1 \pmod p$ would be solvable for y', and $(y'x)^2 + (y'y)^2 \equiv 0 \pmod p$ implies $(y'x)^2 \equiv -1 \pmod p$, whereas -1 is a quadratic nonresidue of p. This shows that m cannot be a prime congruent to 3 (mod 4), in fact, cannot even be congruent to 3 (mod 4), since then it would have such a prime factor.

On the other hand, all primes congruent to 1 (mod 4) are the sums of two squares, as is shown by

Theorem 6.6a. If p is a prime congruent to 1 (mod 4), it can be expressed as a sum of two squares in essentially one and only one way, that is, aside from the order and signs of x and y.

The fact that such a prime is a sum of two squares will follow immediately once the truth of the following statement is established: If s is an integer such that $s^2 \equiv -1 \pmod{p}$, (there is such an s since $p \equiv 1 \pmod 4$ implies $(-1|p) = 1$), then the congruence

(2) $$x \equiv sy \pmod{p}$$

has a solution x_0, y_0 with $|x_0| < \sqrt{p} > |y_0|$. (See Exercise 9 in Section 2.5.) To prove this statement, let x and y range over the values

$$0, 1, 2, \cdots, [\sqrt{p}].$$

Then $x - sy$ takes on

$$\{[\sqrt{p}] + 1\}^2$$

values, that is, more than p different values. Hence two of them must be congruent $\pmod{p}$, and we have

$$x_1 - sy_1 \equiv x_2 - sy_2 \pmod{p}.$$

Thus, if we set $x_0 = x_1 - x_2$, $y_0 = y_1 - y_2$, we see that x_0 and y_0 form a solution of the congruence (2) and x_0^2 and y_0^2 are both less than p. This completes the proof of the statement.

For such a solution of congruence (2), we have

$$0 \equiv (x_0 - sy_0)(x_0 + sy_0) = x_0^2 - s^2 y_0^2 \equiv x_0^2 + y_0^2 \equiv 0 \pmod{p}.$$

That is, $x_0^2 + y_0^2 = kp$. Furthermore, the above statement implies $x_0^2 < p$, $y_0^2 < p$ and hence $x_0^2 + y_0^2 < 2p$. Thus $k = 1$ and p is the sum of the two squares x_0^2 and y_0^2. (Ref. 10, pp. 188 ff.)

To show the uniqueness of the solution, suppose

(3) $$x_1^2 + y_1^2 = p = x_2^2 + y_2^2,$$

where x_1, y_1, x_2, y_2 are all positive integers. Multiply the first equation by y_2^2 and the second by y_1^2, and subtract to get

$$y_2^2 x_1^2 - y_1^2 x_2^2 = p(y_2^2 - y_1^2) \equiv 0 \pmod{p}.$$

Hence

(4) $$y_2 x_1 \equiv \pm y_1 x_2 \pmod{p}.$$

Now, (3) implies that x_1, x_2, y_1, y_2 are all less than p. Thus (4) shows that

$$y_2 x_1 = y_1 x_2 \text{ or } y_2 x_1 + y_1 x_2 = p.$$

If the second equation holds, then $x_1 x_2 - y_1 y_2 = 0$, for multiplication of the equations in (3) gives

$$p^2 = (x_1^2 + y_1^2)(x_2^2 + y_2^2) = (x_1 y_2 + x_2 y_1)^2 + (x_1 x_2 - y_1 y_2)^2.$$

Thus we have shown that (3), with x_1, x_2, y_1, y_2 all positive integers, implies

$$x_1 x_2 = y_1 y_2 \text{ or } y_2 x_1 = y_1 x_2.$$

However, (3) implies that $(x_1, y_1) = 1$, $(x_2, y_2) = 1$, and hence

$$x_1 = y_2, \ x_2 = y_1 \text{ or } x_1 = x_2, y_1 = y_2,$$

and our proof is complete.

Since $x^2 + y^2 = 2$ is obviously solvable, all the above results may be combined in the "if" part of

Theorem 6.6b. A positive integer m is the sum of two squares if and only if every prime factor of m which is congruent to 3 (mod 4) occurs to an even power in m.

Proof: Suppose $p \equiv 3$ (mod 4) and divides m. Then by Lemma 6.6b, $m = x^2 + y^2$ implies $x = px_1$, $y = py_1$, and $m = p^2 m_1$, where

$$m_1 = x_1^2 + y_1^2.$$

If m_1 is divisible by p, it must be divisible by p^2, and so we can continue. If p occurred to an odd power in m, we would eventually have the impossible equation $m_o = x^2 + y^2$ to solve where p, but not p^2, divides m_o. On the other hand, application of Lemma 6.6a shows that all numbers in which the primes congruent to 3 (mod 4) occur to an even power are representable as the sum of two squares.

Exercises 6.6

1. What circles $x^2 + y^2 = m$ have lattice points on them?

2. Prove that if the lengths of the sides of a right triangle are integers whose g.c.d. is 1, all the prime factors of the length of the hypotenuse are congruent to 1 (mod 4).

3. Find for what integers m, the following equation is solvable in integers:

$$x^2 + 2y^2 = m.$$

How many solutions are there when m is a prime?

Bibliography

1. F. E. Andrews, "Revolving Numbers," *Atlantic Monthly*, 155 (1935): 459–466.

2. W. W. R. Ball, *Mathematical Recreations and Essays*, 11th ed., The Macmillan Company, New York, 1939.

3. Harold Davenport, *The Higher Arithmetic*, Hutchinson's University Library, London, 1952.

4. L. E. Dickson, *History of the Theory of Numbers*, Carnegie Institute, Washington, D.C., 1919–1923, Vols. I, II, III.

5. ———, *Introduction to the Theory of Numbers*, University of Chicago Press, Chicago, 1929.

6. G. H. Hardy and E. M. Wright, *An Introduction to the Theory of Numbers*, 2nd ed., Clarendon Press, Oxford, 1945.

7. D. H. Lehmer, *A Guide to Tables in the Theory of Numbers*, National Academy of Sciences, 1941.

8. C. C. MacDuffee, *An Introduction to Abstract Algebra*, John Wiley & Sons, Inc., New York, 1940.

9. H. A. Merrill, *Mathematical Excursions*, Bruce Humphries, Inc., Boston, 1934.

10. Trygve Nagell, *Introduction to Number Theory*, John Wiley & Sons, Inc., New York, 1951.

11. Oystein Ore, *Number Theory and Its History*, McGraw-Hill Book Co., Inc., New York, 1948.

12. B. M. Stewart, *Theory of Numbers*, The Macmillan Company, New York, 1952.

13. J. J. Sylvester, *Collected Mathematical Papers*, Cambridge University Press, London, 1912, Vol. 4, pp. 607–610.

14. J. V. Uspensky and M. A. Heaslet, *Elementary Number Theory*, McGraw-Hill Book Co., Inc., New York, 1939.

15. H. N. Wright, *First Course in Theory of Numbers*, John Wiley & Sons, Inc., New York, 1939.

16. J. W. A. Youngs, *Monographs in Modern Mathematics*, see "On Construction of Regular Polygons," by L. E. Dickson, Longmans, Green & Co., New York, 1911, pp. 374ff.

Index

Index

A

Absolute value, 41
Addition, natural numbers, 3
  negative numbers, 12
  rational numbers, 29
Aliquot parts, 57
Approximations by continued fractions, 89
Associative property, addition, 3
  multiplication, 4

B

Belongs to an exponent, 49
Binary system, 24

C

Cancellation property, fractions, 28
  natural numbers, 7
Character, defined, 121
  quadratic, 121
Chinese remainder theorem, 60
Closure property, addition, 3
  multiplication, 4
Commutative property, addition, 3
  multiplication, 4
Congruence, properties of, 42
Congruence notation, 41
Congruential equations, 45
Conjugate, 97

Continued fractions, infinite, 83
  simple, 82
Convergents of continued fractions, 83
  intermediate, 90

D

Decimals, 31
  periodic (repeating), 38
Determinative property of equality, 3
Diophantine Equation, 62
  linear, 63
  quadratic, 69
Distributive property, 5, 12

E

Eisenstein, 127
Equality, natural numbers, 3
  rational numbers, 28
Euclid algorithm, 16
Euler Phi-function, 48
  properties of, 52
Euler's Criterion, 119
Euler's Theorem, 48

F

Farey Sequence, 92
Fermat's Last Theorem, 73
Fermat's Little Theorem, 46
Fibonacci Sequence, 76

141